VOCABULARY

for the **College Bound**

LEVEL 7

2nd Edition
Revised and Expanded

Prestwick House

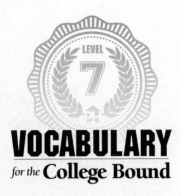

VOCABULARY
for the **College Bound**

Senior Editor: Paul Moliken

Editor: Darlene Gilmore

Cover & Text Design: Larry Knox

Layout: Chris Koniencki

 **Prestwick House**

P.O. Box 658 Clayton, Delaware 19938   www.prestwickhouse.com

Item No. 309272

Printed in the U.S.A.

Table *of* Contents

Strategies for Completing Activities

Lessons

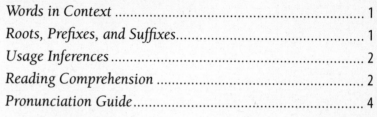

VOCABULARY
for the **College Bound**

Strategies *for* Completing Activities

Words in Context

One way you can make sure that you understand what an unfamiliar word means is to see it used in a sentence and make a guess, an inference, as to its meaning. For example, you probably do not know what the word *theriomorphic* means. Using roots, prefixes, and suffixes will help, as you will see explained below. Read it in the following sentence, though, and you will have another method to arrive at its meaning:

> The drawing on the clay tablet that archaeologists recently discovered depicted a man with antlers and hooves—a *theriomorphic* being—within a ring of fire.

Clues in the sentence enable you to see the context of *theriomorphic*: a primitive drawing showing something not completely human. Therefore, you can infer that *theriomorphic* means "a person who looks like an animal."

Here's another example:

> Dawn was a *somnambulist*; on some nights, her family found her in the hall, other times she was discovered in the basement, and once, they found her sitting asleep in the front seat of the car.

After reading the sentence, you should be able to infer that the word *somnambulist* must mean "someone who walks in his or her sleep."

Roots, Prefixes, and Suffixes

To the person interested in words, a knowledge of roots, prefixes, and suffixes turns each new, unfamiliar word into a puzzle. And while it is a sure and lifelong way to build your vocabulary, there are two points to keep in mind.

1. Some words have evolved through usage so that today's definitions are different from the ones you might have inferred from examination of their roots and/or prefixes. For example, the word *abstruse* contains the prefix *ab–* (away) and the root *trudere* (to thrust) and literally means "to thrust away." But today, the word is used to describe something that is "hard to understand."

2. Occasionally, you may be incorrect about a root. For example, knowing that the root *vin* means "to conquer," you would be correct in concluding that the word *invincible* means "not able to be conquered"; but if you tried to apply that root meaning to the word *vindictive* or *vindicate*, you would miss the actual meaning. So, in analyzing an unfamiliar word, check for other possible roots than the one you first assumed if your inferred meaning doesn't fit the context.

These warnings notwithstanding, a knowledge of roots, prefixes, and suffixes is one of the best ways to build a strong, vital vocabulary.

Usage Inferences

The next method of determining if you understand what a word means is for you to see the word as it might be applied to various situations. Therefore, in a Usage Inference, you need to be able to take the definition you learned into the real world. Remembering the definition and using the word correctly are two different concepts. We supply a series of multiple-choice situations in which you need to figure out the best use of the word.

Let's assume that you learned in a lesson that *specious* means "false or faulty reasoning that seems true" or "an argument that does not stand up to logical reasoning."

Example:

When or where would making a *specious* argument most likely be challenged?
A. on Friday night asking for the keys to the family car
B. in a jury room debating the guilt of someone on trial
C. with your family deciding on the price of a trip to Hawaii
D. at school trying to convince your friend to go sky diving

While all the answers could be examples of making a specious argument, the one that might cause a problem is B, simply because any faulty argument would most likely be argued against by another juror. Obviously, faulty logic and arguments can be used in A, B, C, and D. After all, saying the wrong thing may prevent getting the keys, spending too much could ruin a trip, and sky diving is dangerous. These three situations, though, are less likely to have flawed logic called into question.

Another key to the correct answer is stated in the question, so make sure that you read that part carefully, as it frequently will narrow down your choices.

Reading Comprehension

Reading questions generally fall into several types.

1. *Identifying the main idea or the author's purpose. In short, the question asks, "What is this selection about?"*

In some paragraphs, this is easy to spot because there are one or two ideas that leap from the paragraph. In some selections, however, this may be much more difficult, especially if there are convoluted sentences with clauses embedded within clauses.   It also may be difficult in those selections in which there are inverted sentences (a sentence with the subject at the end) or elliptical sentences (a sentence in which a word or words are left out). All of these obstacles can be overcome if you take one sentence at a time and put it in your own words.

Consider the following sentence:

These writers either jot down their thoughts bit by bit, in short, ambiguous, and para-doxical sentences, which apparently mean much more than they say—of this kind of writing Schelling's treatises on natural philosophy are a splendid instance; or else they hold forth with a deluge of words and the most intolerable diffusiveness, as though no end of fuss were necessary to make the reader understand the deep meaning of their sentences, whereas it is some quite simple if not actually trivial idea, examples of which may be found in plenty in the popular works of Fichte, and the philosophical manuals of a hundred other miserable dunces.

But if we edit out some of the words, the main point of this sentence is obvious.

These writers either jot down their thoughts bit by bit, in short, ambiguous, and para-doxical sentences, which apparently mean much more than they say—of this kind of writing Schelling's treatises on natural philosophy are a splendid instance; or else they hold forth with a deluge of words and the most intolerable diffusiveness, as though [it] end of fuss were necessary to make the reader understand the deep meaning of their sentences, whereas it is some [a] quite simple if not actually trivial idea, examples of which may be found in plenty in the popular works of Fichte, and the philosophical manuals of a hundred other miserable dunces.

While the previous sentence needs only deletions to make it clear, this next one requires major revisions and must be read carefully and put into the reader's own words.

Some in their discourse desire rather commendation of wit, in being able to hold all arguments, than of judgment, in discerning what is true; as if it were a praise to know what might be said, and not what should be thought.

After studying it, a reader might revise the sentence as follows:

In their conversations, some people would rather win praise for their wit or style of saying something rather than win praise for their ability to judge between what is true or false—as if it were better to sound good regardless of the quality of thought.

2. *Identifying the stated or inferred meaning. Simply, what is the author stating or suggesting?*

3. *Identifying the tone or mood of the selection or the author's feeling.*

To answer this type of question, look closely at individual words and their connotations. For example, if an author describes one person as stubborn and another as firm, it tells you something of the author's feelings. In the same manner, if the author uses many words with harsh, negative connotations, he is conveying one mood; but if he uses words with milder negative connotations, he may be striving for quite another mood.

Pronunciation Guide

ă	pat	ō	boat, oh
ā	aid, fey, pay	ŏŏ	took
â	air, care, wear, ant	ōō	boot, fruit
ä	father	ô	ball, haul
b	bib	p	pop
ch	church	r	roar
d	deed	s	miss, sauce, see
ĕ	pet, pleasure	sh	dish, ship
ē	be, bee, easy, leisure	t	tight
f	fast, fife, off, phase, rough	th	path, thin
g	gag	th	this, bathe
h	hat	ŭ	cut, rough
hw	which	û	circle, firm, heard, term, turn, urge, word
ĭ	pit	v	cave, valve, vine
ī	by, guy, pie	w	with
î	dear, deer, fierce, mere	y	yes
j	jury, joke	yōō	abuse, use
k	kiss, clean, quit	z	rose, size, xylophone, zebra
oi	soil, toy	zh	garage, pleasure, vision
ou	cow, out	ə	about, silent, pencil, lemon, circus
ŏ	closet, bother	ər	butter

1. **appall** (ə pôl´) *verb* to fill with horror or amazement; to shock
    The police were *appalled* at the huge number of homicides.
    syn: horrify   *ant:* please, calm, console

2. **blasé** (blŏ zā´) *adj.* uninterested; unexcited
    The millionaire seemed totally *blasé* about the idea of buying three new cars.
    syn: bored   *ant:* awed

3. **feint** (fānt) *verb* to pretend in order to deceive an opponent or divert attention
    away from the real target
    He scored the touchdown by *feinting* left and running right.
    syn: deceive, trick

4. **integral** (ĭn´ tĭ grəl) *adj.* necessary to form a whole
    Bow ties are *integral* parts of tuxedos.
    syn: important   *ant:* unnecessary

5. **lurid** (lŏŏr´ ĭd) *adj.* causing shock or horror
    The victim gave a *lurid,* but accurate, account of the accident.
    syn: shocking, sensational   *ant:* mild

6. **nominal** (nŏm´ ə nəl) *adj.* so small or low in relation to the real value as to be a
    mere token
    The bank transaction carried a *nominal* charge.
    syn: apparent, insignificant   *ant:* actual, notable

7. **persistent** (pər sĭs´ tĕnt) *adj.* lasting; unceasing; persevering; enduring
    The boy was so *persistent* that his parents finally allowed him to go to the party.
    syn: stubborn, determined

8. **seismic** (sīz´ mĭk) *adj.* having a strong or great impact; of, subject to, or caused by
    an earthquake or shock
    Ending the Communist rule in Russia was an event of *seismic* proportions.
    syn: major   *ant:* minor, unimportant

9. **skeptical** (skĕp´ tĭ kəl) *adj.* doubting or disbelieving
    Most people are *skeptical* about the existence of UFOs.
    syn: doubtful   *ant:* convinced

10. **whimsical** (wĭm´ sĭ kəl) *adj.* playful; fanciful
    Cartoons are filled with *whimsical* characters.
    syn: capricious   *ant:* serious

Exercise I Words in Context

Fill in the blanks with the correct vocabulary words needed to complete the sentences.

appall   **blasé**   **skeptical**   **nominal**   **persistent**

A.   When it comes to investing my money, I am very cautious and _____ about new companies. My son, however, is the opposite and invests in a very _____ manner. Some corporations _____ me by their unethical behavior.

B.   Although the telemarketer was _____, I refused the offer, even though she eliminated the _____ $15 sign-up fee.

feint   **whimsical**   **integral**   **lurid**   **seismic**

C.   _____ to the peace treaty was a total surrender.

D.   Most boxers could not _____ as well as Muhammad Ali could.

E.   The new comedy on TV had a funny, _____ character on it.

F.   The earthquake produced _____ shocks felt thousands of miles away.

G.   The _____, gruesome murder made national headlines.

Exercise II Roots, Prefixes, and Suffixes

1. Identify the prefixes in the following words:

    incredible
    unable
    unarmed
    disinterested
    insincere
    intolerant
    uninvolved
    disability
    disadvantage

    The prefixes are *in–*, *un–*, and *dis–*. They all mean "not." In addition, *dis–* can also mean "apart, away." When a word begins with any of these prefixes, the meaning is changed to a negative. List at least two more words for each prefix.

    in _____   un _____   dis _____
    in _____   un _____   dis _____
    in _____   un _____   dis _____

2. Sometimes, *in*, *un*, and *dis* are not prefixes, but are part of the word itself. *Intimate*, *underneath*, and *distinguish* are examples of this. Complete the spaces below with your own examples of words in which *in*, *un*, and *dis* are not prefixes, but are part of the words themselves.

    in _____   un _____   dis _____
    in _____   un _____   dis _____
    in _____   un _____   dis _____

Exercise III Usage Inferences

Choose the answer that best suits the situation.

1. Who would be most blasé about tomorrow's weather?
   A. someone going fishing
   B. a weatherman
   C. a person confined to bed rest
   D. the school principal

2. What should you be most skeptical about?
   A. something too good to be true
   B. a winning ticket in the lottery
   C. your teacher's warning about cheating
   D. something unnecessary to your life

3. Who or what is usually most persistent?
   A. the weather
   B. a dog
   C. a car salesman
   D. a dictionary that is missing pages

Exercise IV Reading Comprehension

Read the selection and answer the questions.

The guanaco, or wild llama, is found on the plains of Patagonia; it is the South American representative of the camel of the East. It is an elegant animal in a state of nature, with a long slender neck and fine legs. It is very common over the whole of the temperate parts of the continent, as far south as the islands near Cape Horn. It generally lives in small herds of from half a dozen to thirty in each; but on the banks of the St. Cruz we saw one herd which must have contained at least five hundred.

They are generally wild and extremely wary. Mr. Stokes told me that he one day saw through a glass a herd of these animals which evidently had been frightened, and were running away at full speed, although their distance was so great that he could not distinguish them with his naked eye. The sportsman frequently receives the first notice of their presence, by hearing from a long distance their peculiar shrill neighing note of alarm. If he then looks attentively, he will probably see the herd standing in a line on the side of some distant hill. On approaching nearer, a few more squeals are given, and off they set at an apparently slow, but really quick canter, along some narrow beaten track to a neighboring hill. If, however, by chance he abruptly meets a single animal, or several together, they will generally stand motionless and intently gaze at him; then perhaps move on a few yards, turn round, and look again.

–*Charles Darwin*

1.　What is the best title for this selection?
   A. What Darwin Found
   B. Traits of Guanacos
   C. Mr. Stokes Spies a Llama
   D. Stalking the Wild Llamas
   E. Patagonian Wildlife

2.　The difference between solitary and herding llamas is that single ones
   A. live in Patagonia.
   B. have longer necks.
   C. are extremely cautious.
   D. are less wary.
   E. can be shot more easily.

3.　Darwin compares the llama to
   A. a quadruped.
   B. a mule.
   C. a camel.
   D. a guanaco.
   E. a herd of buffalo.

4.　According to Darwin, the hunter
   A. can hear the llamas from a distance.
   B. has the advantage of a telescope.
   C. should not shoot these animals.
   D. can catch sight of llamas easily.
   E. needs to sneak up on llamas.

1. **brazen** (brā´ zən) *adj.* rudely bold; impudent
   An elephant usually makes a *brazen* but false charge at an enemy.
   syn: insolent   *ant*: reserved, well-mannered

2. **foster** (fô´ stər) *verb* to promote the development or growth of; to encourage;
      to cultivate
   Schools *foster* good citizenship, as well as education.
   syn: further, aid   *ant*: oppose, restrain

3. **impugn** (ĭm pyōōn´) *verb* to attack as false; to cast doubt on
   It was not necessary to *impugn* the accused's character in court.
   syn: deny   *ant*: authenticate

4. **obsolescence** (ŏb sə lĕs´ ənse) *noun* the state of being no longer useful or in fashion
   Because nearly everyone uses computers, the typewriter may become an example of
   obsolescence.

5. **pretext** (prē´ tĕkst´) *noun* an excuse given to hide the real reason for something
   The officer's *pretext* for searching the car was that he had heard strange sounds coming
   from the trunk.
   syn: excuse, alibi

6. **singular** (sĭng´ gyə lər) *adj.* exceptional
   Superman, not Batman, is the *singular*, most powerful superhero.
   syn: uncommon, unique   *ant*: usual

7. **sobriety** (sə brī´ ĭ tē) *noun* seriousness in bearing, manner, or treatment; the state
      of being sober
   The *sobriety* of the formal hearing made it clear that the committee was taking the
   matter seriously.
                                      ant: lightheartedness, drunkenness

8. **ultimate** (ŭl´ tə mĭt) *adj.* final, conclusive; the highest possible
   The *ultimate* goal of many amateur athletes is Olympic competition.
   syn: last   *ant*: first, beginning

9. **wan** (wŏn) *adj.* unnaturally pale, as from illness; weak or faint
   Many people appear *wan* and tired after a harsh, cold, sunless winter.
   syn: ashen   *ant*: colorful

10. **wane** (wān) *verb* to gradually decrease
    Directly after the moon is full, it begins to *wane*.
    syn: abate, ebb   *ant*: wax, grow

Fill in the blanks with the correct vocabulary words needed to complete the sentences.

impugn	sobriety	ultimate	pretext	brazen

A. In a(n) _____ attempt to _____ the candidate's reputation, his opponent raised questions about the entire family's _____, not just the candidate's.

B. The invention of atomic power was voted the _____ event of the 20th century.

C. The dictator used false claims of invasion as a(n) _____ for war.

obsolescence	wane	wan	foster	singular

D. The _____ difference between the twins is their height. After graduation, the competition between the two began to _____ gradually, and their new-found ease with each other was finally able to _____ peace within the family.

E. "You look rather _____, even after a week in the sun," claimed my neighbor.

F. Complicated machinery frequently breaks down because of _____, not complexity.

Exercise II Roots, Prefixes, and Suffixes

1. What is the common root for the following words?

   technology
   technique
   technicality

   The root *tech* means "skill," "art," or "craft." Therefore, when a word contains this root, it has to do with some sort of ability.

   List any words you can think of that contain *tech*.

   _____   _____   _____

   _____   _____   _____

   _____   _____   _____

2. What is the common root for these words?

   revert
   convert
   vertigo
   subvert
   vertex

   The root is *vert*, and it means "turn." In the dictionary, look up the five words above to see how each word is derived from Latin and how each has the meaning of "turn."

Choose the answer that best suits the situation.

1. Who are the most *brazen*?
   A. lawyers
   B. TV hosts
   C. lottery winners
   D. telemarketers

2. Which of the following *wanes*?
   A. flooded rivers
   B. tall trees
   C. mountain ranges
   D. blue skies

3. What would *foster* students' creativity in a writing class?
   A. a personal essay
   B. a novel summary
   C. a multiple-choice test
   D. an author biography

Read the selection and answer the questions.

There is a spider crawling along the floor in the room where I sit; he runs with heedless, hurried haste, he hobbles awkwardly towards me, he stops—he sees the giant shadow before him, and, at a loss whether to retreat or proceed, meditates his huge foe—but since I do not stand up and seize him, as he would seize a hapless fly within his web, he takes heart, and ventures on with mingled cunning, impudence, and fear. As he passes me, I lift up the rug to assist his escape, for I am glad to get rid of the unwelcome intruder, and shudder at the recollection after he is gone. A child, a woman, a clown, or a moralist a century ago, would have crushed the little reptile to death—my philosophy has got beyond that—I bear the creature no ill-will, but still I hate the very sight of it. The spirit of malevolence survives the practical exertion of it. We learn to curb our will and keep our overt actions within the bounds of humanity, long before we can subdue our sentiments and imaginations to the same mild tone. We give up the external demonstration, the brute violence, but cannot part with the essence or principle of hostility.

–William Hazlitt

1. What is the main idea of this selection?
   A. People generally hate spiders.
   B. It is wrong to hate.
   C. Hatred of evil is acceptable.
   D. Spiders are examples of peoples' hatred.
   E. People show hatred through emotions, not actions.

2. Which word does Hazlitt use to describe the spider?
   A. fly
   B. reptile
   C. moralist
   D. giant
   E. ill-will

3. Why does the author not kill the spider?
   A. He is not a cruel person.
   B. He does not act on impulse.
   C. He does not hate spiders.
   D. His philosophy has matured.
   E. He would rather allow it to live.

4. This passage examines differences between
   A. spiders and men.
   B. evil and hatred.
   C. hatred and love.
   D. past and present.
   E. action and thought.

1. **astute** (ə stōōt´) *adj.* keen in judgment
An *astute* tenant does not sign a contract before reading it.
syn: shrewd   *ant:* gullible, naïve

2. **duress** (də rĕs´) *noun* constraint by threat; coercion
The spy did not confess, even under *duress*.
syn: force

3. **imperturbable** (ĭm pər tûr´ bə bəl) *adj.* not easily disturbed; unshakable; calm
A paramedic needs to be *imperturbable* or find a new job.
syn: cool, composed   *ant:* touchy, testy

4. **innate** (ĭn āt´) *adj.* possessed from birth; inborn; inherent
Some religions teach that everyone has an *innate* goodness.
syn: natural   *ant:* acquired

5. **jurisdiction** (jŏŏr ĭs dĭk´ shən) *noun* the authority to interpret and apply the law
The state police's *jurisdiction* ends at the border.

6. **potential** (pə tĕn´ shəl) *noun* an ability that may or may not be developed
Because of a poor attitude, the student never fulfilled his *potential*.
syn: possibility   *ant:* actuality

7. **premise** (prĕm´ ĭs) *noun* a statement upon which an argument is based or from which a conclusion is drawn
One of the first *premises* of American society is that all people are equal.
syn: assumption

8. **profane** (prō fān´) *adj.* showing contempt for God or sacred things
For years, the churches claimed any music not praising holiness was *profane*.
syn: impious, irreverent   *ant:* holy; pious

9. **unkempt** (ŭn kĕmpt´) *adj.* not neat or tidy
During his absence, his lawn took on an *unkempt* appearance.
syn: sloppy

10. **vapid** (vă´ pĭd) *adj.* uninteresting; flat; stale
The wiretap revealed nothing but meaningless, *vapid* conversations.
syn: flavorless, insipid   *ant:* meaningful, zesty

Fill in the blanks with the correct vocabulary words needed to complete the sentences.

| innate | vapid | astute | imperturbable | premise |

A.   The bigot's basic _____ is that one race is superior to another. This _____ assumption has no basis in fact. A more _____ reasoning would be that all races are equal and that individuals vary in their _____ qualities.

B.   The stuntman looked _____ in the face of extreme danger.

| duress | jurisdiction | potential | profane | unkempt |

C.   The _____ vagrant was arrested, but he claimed the police had no _____ over him.

D.   The young child's _____ words surprised his parents.

E.   The prisoner of war claimed the confession he signed was made under _____ and torture.

F.   The drought greatly increased the _____ for forest fires.

Exercise II Roots, Prefixes, and Suffixes

What suffix do the following words have in common?

debatable
reliable
callable
conceivable
miserable

This suffix means exactly what it says: "able to...." A variation of –able is –ible, which means the same, as in visible or horrible.

In nearly all cases, these two suffixes mean "capable of" or "able to." Can you find at least 10 other words that use these suffixes?

_____able   _____ible
_____able   _____ible
_____able   _____ible
_____able   _____ible
_____able   _____ible

Exercise III Usage Inferences

Choose the answer that best suits the situation.

1.   What is a likely premise for a fight?
      A. a car race
      B. a party
      C. a missing dog
      D. an insult

2.   Which one is most imperturbable?
      A. a politician campaigning for re-election
      B. a mountain climber
      C. a person who is prepared
      D. a pilot during wartime

3.   Which would be most likely to cause duress?
      A. handcuffs
      B. playfulness
      C. automobiles
      D. wisdom

Read the selection and answer the questions.

A recent study reported that every five days an American child chokes to death on food, and the food most often choked on is the hot dog.

"If you were trying to design something that would be perfect to block a child's airway, it would be a bite-size piece of hot dog," says Dr. Susan P. Baker of Johns Hopkins University in Baltimore. Because they are round and soft, pieces of hot dog can easily plug the airway that opens into the esophagus. All a child has to do is cough, choke, or laugh while he is eating.

"A child under the age of four should not be given a whole hot dog to eat," Dr. Baker said. "Neither should they be cut crosswise. Most parents don't know that."

More than 40 percent of food choking deaths among children are caused by hot dogs, candy, nuts, or grapes, Dr. Baker reported in Friday's issue of the Journal of the American Medical Association. Half the choking deaths in infants younger than 12 months were caused by hot dogs, apple pieces, cookies, or biscuits.

Among one-year-olds—who suffered the highest incidents of food asphyxiation of all groups—carrots and hot dogs were most often the cause, the study found. Grapes and peanuts were the most frequent causes of fatal choking among two-year-olds. Among three-year-olds, only ten food fatalities occurred, but seven of them were blamed on hot dogs, the doctors said.

Dr. Baker recommended the following safety measures: change the shape of products to make them less dangerous; provide warning labels on packages; and put out information on high-risk foods to reduce the number of childhood choking cases.

A spokeswoman for Oscar Mayer Food said her company has looked into choking risks associated with hot dogs but has not modified its product or labels. "We feel that the major cause of the problem is lack of parental supervision when the children are eating," she said.

1. The best title for this article is
    A. Dangerous Foods.
    B. Don't Give Hot Dogs to Kids.
    C. Hot Dogs Can Kill.
    D. Cut Up Those Dogs.
    E. Parents Should Observe Children's Food.

2. Which group had the most food deaths?
    A. three-year-olds
    B. two-year-olds
    C. one-year-olds
    D. The article does not say.
    E. infants under 12 months old.

3. What can you infer from paragraph three?
    A. Dr. Baker is a pediatric doctor.
    B. Dr. Baker wants to prevent accidents.
    C. Dr. Baker feels children under four should not eat hot dogs.
    D. All of the above are correct.
    E. Both A and C are correct.

4. The hot dog spokesperson is
    A. not concerned over the deaths.
    B. a woman.
    C. putting warning labels on the food.
    D. going to change the shape of the food.
    E. None of the above is correct.

Lesson Four

1. **disperse** (dǐ spûrs´) *verb* to scatter
    One drop of crude oil can be *dispersed* over gallons of fresh water.
    syn: dispense, spread   *ant:* gather

2. **drudgery** (drŭj´ ə rē) *noun* difficult work
    He quit his boring job because of the *drudgery*.
    syn: labor, tediousness

3. **feudal** (fyōōd´ l) *adj.* primitive or pertaining to the Middle Ages
    No matter how rich the owner was, *feudal* castles were always cold.

4. **fray** (frā) *noun* a fight
    Eager to join the *fray*, the player's teammate punched someone.
    syn: brawl, scuffle

5. **jostle** (jŏs´əl) *verb* to bump
    The last bowling pin had not been *jostled* enough to fall.
    syn: push, shove

6. **mundane** (mŭn dān´) *adj.* worldly rather than spiritual; ordinary, routine
    Everyday *mundane* routines bored him.
    syn: commonplace   *ant:* extraordinary

7. **paltry** (pôl´ trē) *adj.* meager; insignificant
    We bought the food wholesale for a *paltry* amount of money.
    syn: small, measly   *ant:* significant

8. **saturate** (sach´ ə rāt) *verb* to soak; to infuse
    Because the farmers had *saturated* the food with pesticides, we dared not eat it.
    syn: drench   *ant:* dry out

9. **scurry** (skûr´ ē) *verb* to dash
    The bugs *scurried* in all directions when the light came on.
    syn: scuttle, dart

10. **vogue** (vōg) *noun* fashion
    The fashions in *vogue* today may be very outdated next season.
    syn: style, trend

Exercise I Words in Context

Fill in the blanks with the correct vocabulary words needed to complete the sentences.

| scurry | paltry | drudgery | feudal | saturate |

A. The servant's _____ each day was paid for with a _____ sum of money. She would _____ around the castle all day long, tired of the _____ system that had made her a serf.

B. Before cooking this meal, you must _____ the pan with oil.

| disperse | vogue | jostled | fray | mundane |

C. Years ago, proms in middle school were rare, but now they are very much in _____ .

D. Ignore the _____ issues and concentrate on the important ones.

E. After a mild _____ had broken out during the football game, the police used tear gas to _____ the crowd. In the confusion, people _____ one another in an effort to move away.

Exercise II Roots, Prefixes, and Suffixes

1. What root is used in the following three words?

   contraband
   contradictory
   contrary

   The root *contra* means "against." Usually, when a word has *contra* in it, it refers to being opposed to or in opposition to.

   List three other words that use *contra* as their root.

   _____   _____   _____

2. Now, list a few words that have *contra* in them that do not mean "against," like *contraction*.

   _____   _____   _____

Choose the answer that best suits the situation.

1. Which would be the best example of a *paltry* amount or number?
   A. feathers in a pillow
   B. a $20 computer
   C. novels with 500 pages
   D. the muscles in your body

2. What would most likely be *dispersed*?
   A. snowmen in the sun
   B. cars on the turnpike
   C. birds being shot at
   D. someone at an ATM

3. Someone who experiences *drudgery* would look
   A. excited and eager.
   B. exhausted and tired.
   C. energetic, but bored.
   D. happy, but worried.

Read the selection and answer the questions.

I know that in writing the following pages I am divulging the great secret of my life, the secret which for some years I have guarded far more carefully than any of my earthly possessions; and it is a curious study to me to analyze the motives which prompt me to do it. I feel that I am led by the same impulse which forces the unfound-out criminal to take somebody into his confidence, although he knows that the act is liable, even almost certain, to lead to his undoing. I know that I am playing with fire, and I feel the thrill which accompanies that most fascinating pastime; and, back of it all, I think I find a sort of savage and diabolical desire to gather up all the little tragedies of my life, and turn them into a practical joke on society.

And, too, I suffer a vague feeling of unsatisfaction, of regret, of almost remorse from which I am seeking relief, and of which I shall speak in the last paragraph of this account.

I was born in a little town of Georgia a few years after the close of the Civil War. I shall not mention the name of the town, because there are people still living there who could be connected with this narrative. I have only a faint recollection of the place of my birth. At times I can close my eyes, and call up in a dream-like way things that seem to have happened ages ago in some other world. I can see in this half vision a little house,—I am quite sure it was not a large one;—I can remember that flowers grew in the front yard, and that around each bed of flowers was a hedge of vary-colored glass bottles stuck in the ground neck down. I remember that once, while playing around in the sand, I became curious to know whether or not the bottles grew as the flowers did, and I proceeded to dig them up to find out; the investigation brought me a terrific spanking which indelibly fixed the incident in my mind.

–James Johnson

1. The "I" in this selection reveals emotions of
   A. worry and joy.
   B. sadness and anticipation.
   C. curiosity and unhappiness.
   D. relief and hatred.
   E. calmness and anger.

2. The name of the town where the author was born is not discussed because
   A. his parents still live there.
   B. every reader would recognize it.
   C. it is in Georgia.
   D. he cannot recall it.
   E. people in the story are still in the town.

3. The author received a punishment for
    A. revealing names.
    B. throwing bottles.
    C. practical joking.
    D. ruining a flower bed.
    E. Both B and D are correct.

4. The best title for the *first paragraph only* would be
    A. Why I Write.
    B. A Secret to Come.
    C. Sharing the Unknown.
    D. Earthly Possessions.
    E. Thrills and Tragedies.

1. **constraint** (kən strānt´) *noun* force; coercion
I realize that you may be upset, Bob, but show some *constraint* and behave yourself.
syn: restraint

2. **contrive** (kən trīv´) *verb* to plot
The swindler *contrived* ways to cheat the government.
syn: concoct, devise

3. **dupe** (dōōp) *verb* to fool; to delude
Many sweepstakes use trickery to *dupe* people into entering.
syn: hoax, trick

4. **equilibrium** (ē kwə lĭb´ rē əm) *noun* balance; stability
Mark Twain achieved the perfect *equilibrium* between humor and satire.
syn: steadiness, evenness   *ant:* imbalance

5. **exponential** (ĕk spə nĕn´ shəl) *adj.* increasing rapidly
The universe has expanded in an *exponential* fashion since it began.

6. **obstinate** (ŏb´ stə nĭt) *adj.* stubborn
He argued with his mother about staying out late, but she was *obstinate* and set a curfew.
syn: bull-headed   *ant:* pliable

7. **pantheon** (pan´ thē ŏn) *noun* a group of highly regarded people; a place for such people; a range
The *pantheon* of religions goes from Animism to Zoroastrianism.

8. **placard** (plak´ ərd) *noun* a sign
Many men on strike held handwritten *placards*.
syn: poster

9. **sally** (sal´ ē) *noun* a rush or leap forward
The enemy's first *sally* surprised the troops camped by the river.

10. **tranquil** (trang´ kwəl) *adj.* calm
The Pacific Ocean is not *tranquil* at all, yet its name does mean "calm."
syn: placid   *ant:* agitated

Fill in the blanks with the correct vocabulary words needed to complete the sentences.

dupe   **contrived**   **obstinate**   **equilibrium**   **pantheon**

A.   "We tried to _____ him out of his money," said the swindlers, "but he was so _____ that we gave up."

B.   Zeus sat at the head of the _____ of Greek gods.

C.   An ear infection can cause a loss of _____.

D.   The children _____ a swing simply from three hanging vines.

placard   **sally**   **exponential**   **constraints**   **tranquil**

E.   The night was so _____ and warm that I decided to take a walk.

F.   The _____ advertised a big sale at the furniture store.

G.   Inflation can cause prices to rise in a(n) _____ manner.

H.   Many _____ were heaped upon the boy for violating curfew.

I.   The team's opening _____ on field day was met with fierce resistance.

Exercise II Roots, Prefixes, and Suffixes

1.   What prefix is common to the following words?

transatlantic
translation
transfer
transmit

You can easily see that the prefix is *trans–*. It means "across." List at least 5 more words using this prefix.

_____   _____   _____

_____   _____

2. A set of useful prefixes is *hypo–* and *hyper–*. These are easily confused; one (*hypo–*) means "under," and the other (*hyper–*) means "over" or "above." A needle under your skin is a _____*dermic*. Another word for high blood pressure (above normal), is _____*tension*. List some words you already know that use these prefixes.

hyper _____   hypo_____

hyper _____   hypo_____

hyper _____   hypo_____

Exercise III Usage Inferences

Choose the answer that best suits the situation.

1. Who would be more likely to have *constraints* placed on him?
   A. a bee collector
   B. a restaurant owner
   C. someone who disputed a ticket in court
   D. a criminal

2. An *obstinate* dog might most likely
   A. do many tricks well.
   B. bark at strangers.
   C. disobey its owner.
   D. have puppies each year.

3. Which would be the best example of something that is *tranquil*?
   A. a woman holding the winning lottery ticket
   B. a player before a game
   C. a person fishing in a lake
   D. a day before SAT scores come out

Read the selection and answer the questions.

For years, farmers have known that pigs love to play with toys. They also know that pigs that are given toys to play with are healthier, calmer, and easier to handle. Now research has set out to discover exactly which type of toys pigs prefer.

"There is no point in wasting money on toys for pigs if the pigs are not going to play with them," said Peter Knight, a biologist who studies animal behavior. He has been studying pigs for the past seven years. Through his research he hopes to find ways to boost America's production of high-quality pork.

"People think of pigs as being fat, stupid, dirty animals, who spend most of their time lying in the mud eating," said Knight. "The fact is pigs are one of the smartest of all animals. They are certainly much smarter than dogs. But if they are just kept penned up all the time with nothing to do, they get bored and frustrated. In this, they are just like people."

Knight explained that pigs that are bored tend to get into fights. They bite each other's tails and otherwise hurt each other. In addition, they are harder to get ready for market and more difficult to unload for the slaughterhouse.

More importantly, however, "pigs that get excited and violent tend to produce poor quality meat." Giving them toys keeps their minds occupied. "This way they stay calmer and don't get into fights," said Knight.

But what kind of toys do pigs prefer? According to Knight's research, two of the toys which are favorites among farmers are not favorites with the pigs. "Farmers often give pigs bowling balls," said Knight. "At first, the pigs enjoy butting against them with their heads, and rolling the balls around their pens. But eventually, the balls become coated with manure. Then the pigs ignore them."

Another old favorite of farmers who raise pigs is the dangling chain. This is left hanging over the pig's pen. "We found that chains were too heavy and hurt the pigs' mouths. They much prefer strips of cloth or rubber hoses hanging above their pens," said Knight.

According to Knight, some pigs chew on the ends of the cloth or hoses like chewing gum. Others jerk and shake them the way a puppy shakes a rag doll. "When the pigs have toys they like, they play with them regularly," said Knight. "When we first introduced them to toys, they played with them for about an hour a day. After a week or so, they gradually tapered off to about a half an hour a day of intense activity."

Knight's findings are already being put into practice by some hog raisers. "It is a heck of a lot cheaper to give the pigs a few old rubber hoses than it is to buy them bowling balls," said Gene Green of Wisconsin. Green has raised hogs for 15 years.

"And if it keeps the pigs happy, then I'll have less trouble with them and they will get into fewer fights. I'm putting in some rubber hoses for them today."

The second phase of Knight's research starts soon. Now he is trying to determine if the kind of toys the pigs plays with affects the quality and quantity of meat the pig produces. "We know that giving the pigs toys doesn't *hurt* weight gain, but we don't know yet whether it will *help* weight gain," he said.

1.   What fact is not in the article?
    A. Pigs like toys.
    B. Pigs are smarter than dogs.
    C. Pigs gain weight through playing with toys.
    D. Farmers first used bowling balls as pig toys.
    E. Pigs never fight.

2.   How are hanging chains different from hanging cloth?
    A. Pigs prefer the metal.
    B. Chains interfere with the bowling balls.
    C. Cloth can fall into the pens.
    D. Chains hurt pigs' mouths.
    E. Chains are harder to hang.

3.   Gene Green has
    A. determined that pork tastes better if pigs are content.
    B. raised pigs for 15 years.
    C. seen pigs bite each other's tails.
    D. experimented first with chains.
    E. disagrees with Knight's findings.

4.   What can you infer from the article?
    A. Pigs are easily bored.
    B. Hogs prefer hoses to chains.
    C. Happy hogs make for better meat.
    D. All of the above are correct.
    E. Both A and B are correct.

1. **assail**   (ə sāl´)   *verb*   to attack
    While the Army *assailed* the enemy from the inland side, the Navy hit the coast.
    syn: assault   *ant*: retreat

2. **assets**   (as´ ĕts)   *noun*   resources or wealth
    All his financial and business *assets* belonged to his wife.
    syn: credits, money   *ant*: liabilities, handicaps

3. **cope**   (kōp)   *verb*   to deal with
    It's easier to *cope* with success than failure.
    syn: manage

4. **potent**   (pōt´ nt)   *adj.*   powerful
    The *potent* medicine worked quickly to cure Jenna's illness.
    syn: strong   *ant*: weak

5. **saga**   (sä´ gə)   *noun*   a story; tale
    One of the most well-known movie *sagas* is the *Star Trek* series.
    syn: epic

6. **spontaneous**   (spŏn tā´ nē əs)   *adj.*   happening without an external cause
    When the magician and his assistant disappeared, the audience gave them a *spontaneous* ovation.
    syn: self-generated, unplanned   *ant*: premeditated

7. **stunt**   (stŭnt)   *verb*   to limit growth
    A lack of proper nutrition can *stunt* a child's growth.
    syn: dwarf, check

8. **taut**   (tôt)   *adj.*   tight; tense
    The play's dialogue was so taut *that* people in the audience were on the edge of their seats.
    syn: rigid   *ant*: loose, slack

9. **valor**   (val´ ər)   *noun*   bravery
    The soldiers were rewarded for their *valor* in the battle.
    syn: courage   *ant*: cowardice

10. **wither**   (wĭth´ ər)   *verb*   to dry up; to shrivel
    The young plants *withered* without water.
    syn: wilt, shrink   *ant*: flourish

Exercise I Words in Context

Fill in the blanks with the correct vocabulary words needed to complete the sentences.

wither	**valor**	**taut**	**stunt**	**assail**

A.   They were able to successfully _____ the fortress only because of the great _____ of many soldiers.

B.   Planting a tree in a small space may _____ its growth.

C.   During droughts, many fruits _____ on the vines.

D.   "Pull that line _____," yelled the boss.

assets	**cope**	**potent**	**saga**	**spontaneous**

E.   Beware of the snake's _____ venom.

F.   Because the government's seizure of all their _____ plunged them into poverty, the couple could not _____ with life.

G.   _____ applause broke out during the song.

H.   The _____ of Ulysses' twenty-year journey was written by Homer.

Exercise II Roots, Prefixes, and Suffixes

communism
consumerism
materialism
impressionism
baptism
capitalism

1.   The suffix on all these words, *–ism*, means "a theory, action, or characteristic." Many words have this suffix attached to them. List 5 words you know that have *–ism* on the end.

_____ ism   _____ ism
_____ ism   _____ ism
_____ ism

2. Another suffix, –*ary*, means "related to" or "connected to."

   complimentary – related to a compliment
   coronary – related to the heart
   literary – related to letters or words
   parliamentary – connected with a parliament
   military – related to war

   List 5 words that end in the suffix –*ary*.

   _____ ary   _____ ary
   _____ ary   _____ ary
   _____ ary

Exercise III Usage Inferences

Choose the answer that best suits the situation.

1. Which is the best example of a *saga*?
   A. voting for the president
   B. the *Star Wars* trilogy
   C. a five-course meal
   D. traveling to New Jersey from New York

2. Which person shows the most *valor*?
   A. someone who places a bet for more than he can afford
   B. a woman who stands up for her beliefs
   C. someone who prepares a special meal for his family
   D. a bank robber who has a gun

3. Which situation is the least *spontaneous*?
   A. a wedding with many guests
   B. a surprise quiz in English
   C. saying "I love you" to your parents
   D. rain on a very cloudy day

Read the selection and answer the questions.

For a quarter, visitors to Clyde Peeling's Reptileland can watch a little door open, a live cricket fall into a terrarium, and a frog gobble up the insect. "But the machine was not made to thrill sick people," Peeling said. "Rather, it was made to educate people about a fact of life. In nature there are hunters and the hunted, the predators and the prey."

"No one has made a machine that dispenses live animals to predators before," said Peeling, 41, who has owned the two-acre reptile zoo for 20 years. "I see it as an educational tool. It is not only good because the amphibians and reptiles get to eat live insects, but you have to make people face the facts. If you eat a hamburger, someone has to kill a cow," he said.

While some people find the idea repulsive, some zoo curators see it as a possible answer to two of their big problems. John Behler of the City Zoo said, "The two biggest problems facing zoos are educating the public and feeding the animals. This machine does both; it has some exciting possibilities," he said.

Behler, who plans to buy three cricket machines for the City Zoo, said even people drawn to the machines for entertainment will walk away with a valuable lesson. "Whoever is doing this activity will learn the value of insectivores and the large number of insects, often harmful, they eat. Whether from fun or entertainment, they will learn a valuable lesson."

Peeling said he began talking with his father about developing the machine several years ago. He got the idea after getting fed up with zoo visitors complaining about listless reptiles. "Some animals, if there is nothing to eat, there is nothing to do. It occurred to me that if we could feed them in some way acceptable to the public, it would go over big."

1. Why was the machine developed?
    A. to make money
    B. to make animals seem less lazy
    C. to feed some animals
    D. A, B, and C are correct.
    E. Both B and C are correct.

2. Which pair of words describes the same thing?
    A. insectivore, curator
    B. predator, prey
    C. curator, listless
    D. repulsive, reptile
    E. hunters, predators

3. Peeling
   A. bought the idea of the machine from his father.
   B. owns a reptile zoo.
   C. wants to thrill people.
   D. earns a lot of money from his machine.
   E. All of the above are correct.

4. What point is made about cows?
   A. Cows do not eat insects.
   B. Cows should be in some zoos.
   C. Cows are slaughtered for meat.
   D. Cows are no different from crickets.
   E. People should not eat cows.

1. **badger** (baj´ ər) *verb* to bother
   Even though it was weaned, the young colt still *badgered* his mother for milk.
   syn: hound, plague

2. **belittle** (bĭ lĭt´l) *verb* to criticize; to diminish
   The drill sergeant constantly *belittled* the new recruits.
   syn: disparage, detract   *ant*: magnify, praise

3. **concoct** (kən kŏkt´) *verb* to contrive; to devise
   The writers *concocted* a new dilemma for the hero to overcome each week.
   syn: invent, conceive

4. **realm** (rĕlm) *noun* the range; scope
   His outrageous lie was so far beyond the *realm* of reality that we laughed aloud.
   syn: world

5. **rejuvenate** (rĭ jōō´ və nāt) *verb* to make energetic or feel youthful again
   The trip to Hawaii *rejuvenated* the overworked housewife.
   syn: renew

6. **savory** (sā´ və rē) *adj.* tempting; tasty
   The restaurant's desserts were so *savory* that we had seconds.
   syn: sweet, fragrant   *ant*: unpalatable

7. **scrutinize** (skrōōt´ n īz) *verb* to examine
   Internal Revenue Service agents needed to *scrutinize* the company's records.
   syn: study

8. **spew** (spyōō) *verb* to spit out
   The bank robber *spewed* curses at the police.
   syn: gush

9. **terminal** (tûr´ mə nəl) *adj.* the last
   He paid the full fare and rode the bus until the *terminal* stop.
   syn: final   *ant*: first, beginning

10. **undermine** (ŭn dər mīn´) *verb* to weaken; to ruin
    During war, each side attempts to *undermine* and eventually destroy its enemy's will to fight.
    syn: wreck, thwart   *ant*: reinforce

Fill in the blanks with the correct vocabulary words needed to complete the sentences.

concoct	badger	spewed	terminal	savory

A.   The kitchen emitted many _____ smells; each day, the chefs tried to _____ new recipes.

B.   A period is the _____ punctuation mark of declarative sentences.

C.   "Don't _____ me with your ridiculous demands," screamed the director to the spoiled actress.

D.   The erupting volcano _____ tons of lava on the village.

realm	undermined	rejuvenated	belittle	scrutinize

E.   Marine biologists _____ the underwater _____ to find new species.

F.   The chemical spill near the laboratory _____ years of work.

G.   His new artificial knee _____ the elderly man's spirits.

H.   If you constantly _____ your friends, you can expect to lose them.

1. The prefix *pre–* means "before," "ahead," or "in front of." Without using a dictionary, try to define the following words:

    1. prejudice   _____
    2. prefix   _____
    3. premedical   _____
    4. predetermine   _____
    5. precook   _____

2. The prefix *post–* means the opposite of *pre–*. Use a dictionary to define each of the following words:

    1. posthumous   _____
    2. posterior   _____
    3. postmortem   _____
    4. postpartum   _____

Exercise III Usage Inferences

Choose the answer that best suits the situation.

1. Which is most likely to be *scrutinized*?
   A. a CD collection
   B. a new puppy
   C. your job application
   D. the phone book

2. A person who makes a *concoction* is most likely
   A. a plumber.
   B. a bartender.
   C. a computer salesman.
   D. a dog trainer.

3. Which one is most likely to be *undermined* by stormy weather?
   A. plans to take a nap
   B. an airline flight
   C. buying a ticket for a play
   D. a visit next door

Read the selection and answer the questions.

Every year the United States sends billions of dollars overseas for foreign aid and military operations trying to bring peace and prosperity to troubled regions around the world. Your help often comes too late and seldom alleviates the root of the problem.

Overcrowding and rapid population growth exacerbates many causes of conflict around the world, like ethnic tensions, economic disparity, and struggle over scarce resources. The population of our planet has ballooned rapidly from 2 billion in 1935 to over 6 billion today, and will reach 8 billion by 2025. Ninety percent of this growth will occur in the most troubled regions of the Third World, increasing their already difficult tasks of peace and economic development.

–Helmut Kohl

1. The main idea expressed here is
    A. the U.S. spends money wastefully.
    B. world population is a problem.
    C. a scarcity of natural resources exists.
    D. the Third World has numerous problems.
    E. foreign military aid is unnecessary.

2. In the passage, the word *exacerbates* probably means
    A. increases.
    B. decreases.
    C. worsens.
    D. lessens.
    E. improves.

3. World population in 1935 was approximately
    A. 2 billion.
    B. 4 billion.
    C. 6 billion.
    D. 8 billion.
    E. The answer cannot be determined.

4. According to the passage, peace is hurt by
    A. ethnic tensions.
    B. scarce resources.
    C. economic problems.
    D. expanding population.
    E. All of the above are correct.

1. **buff** (bŭf) *noun* an enthusiast
    The knowledgeable art *buff* somehow mistook a Rembrandt for a fake.
    syn: fan, aficionado

2. **candor** (kan´dər) *noun* honesty; directness
    His *candor* and friendliness impressed everyone who knew him.
    syn: truthfulness   *ant*: deceit

3. **composure** (kəm pō´zhər) *noun* calmness
    In a fire, keep your *composure* and do not panic.
    syn: coolness   *ant*: agitation

4. **condolence** (kən dō´ləns) *noun* sympathy
    The funeral director offered *condolences* to relatives of the deceased.
    syn: compassion   *ant*: harshness

5. **prestigious** (prĕ stĭ´jəs) *adj.* famous; notable
    I once received a *prestigious* award for my essay on politics.
    syn: distinguished   *ant*: unknown

6. **procrastinate** (prō kras´tə nāt) *verb* to delay; put off
    The test was tomorrow, but Dallas *procrastinated* studying for it until the last minute.
    syn: postpone

7. **replenish** (rĭ plĕn´ĭsh) *verb* to restore
    Our dog loves biscuits, and we must *replenish* her supply weekly.
    syn: replace   *ant*: deplete

8. **repress** (rĭ prĕs´) *verb* to suppress; to control
    The majority frequently tries to *repress* the rights of the minority.
    syn: restrain   *ant*: aid, support

9. **ruse** (rōōz) *noun* a trick; ploy
    Children's games are filled with *ruses* and surprises.
    syn: maneuver, gimmick

10. **ruthless** (rōōth´lĭs) *adj.* merciless; grim
    We were put on a *ruthless* program of exercise and diet.
    syn: cruel, heartless   *ant*: humane, compassionate

Exercise I Words in Context

Fill in the blanks with the correct vocabulary words needed to complete the sentences.

ruthless   **repress**   **ruse**   **condolence**   **candor**

A. One _____ gangster used a clever _____ to avoid capture; he had his gang members send letters of _____ to his wife to convince police that he had been killed.

B. The psychiatrist told her patient not to _____ any emotions but to express them with complete _____.

procrastinate   **buff**   **composure**   **replenish**   **prestigious**

C. He was accepted to a _____ university.

D. If you _____ much longer, you'll miss your deadline.

E. After exercise, _____ your body's store of water.

F. The Civil War _____ discovered a relic of Gettysburg on his property and totally lost his _____ because of it.

Exercise II Roots, Prefixes, and Suffixes

1. What is the common root in the following words, and what do you think the root means?

    territorial

    terrain

    terrace

    terrarium

    Mediterranean

    The root *terr* means "earth" or "land." All the words above refer to that idea. The prefix *medi*– in the last word means "middle"; as such, a few thousand years ago, the Mediterranean Sea must have been considered the _____ of the _____ .

2. List at least 5 words that use *terr* to mean "land" and a few that do not.

    _____   _____   _____

    _____   _____   _____

Exercise III Usage Inferences

Choose the answer that best suits the situation.

1. Which example of *repression* is the worst?
    A. "You may not watch television for a week."
    B. The computer constantly shuts down.
    C. No religious worship is allowed in China.
    D. "Wear sunscreen daily or stay inside!"

2. Which is an example of a statement of *candor*?
    A. "I'm sorry, but I can't tell you why."
    B. "You are prettier than anyone I've ever seen."
    C. "My dog ate my homework."
    D. "Yes, I took the money."

3. Who is most likely to use a *ruse*?
    A. a thief
    B. a policeman
    C. a car salesman
    D. a dancer

Exercise IV Reading Comprehension

Read the selection and answer the questions.

Smokeless tobacco use also predicts other drug use. In a study of more than 3,000 male adolescents interviewed twice at nine-month intervals about their use of various psychoactive substances, the main findings were that (1) smokeless tobacco users were significantly more likely to use cigarettes, marijuana, or alcohol than nonusers were, (2) users of smokeless tobacco were significantly more likely to take up the use of these other substances by the second interview if they were not using them at the first, and (3) adolescents who were using any of these substances at the first interview were significantly more likely to increase their use of the substance if they also used smokeless tobacco.

Two other facts are important to consider when evaluating the role of smokeless tobacco products in the use of cigarettes and other substances. First, the overall impact of smokeless tobacco is currently limited primarily to males (the main users of these substances). Second, smokeless tobacco users tend to initiate their tobacco use at about the same age as cigarette smokers or at a slightly earlier age.

1. The best title for this article is
    A. Smoking Leads to Drug Use.
    B. Tobacco Usage Increases with Age.
    C. Smokeless Tobacco Use on the Rise.
    D. Smokeless Tobacco Use Predicts Other Drug Use.
    E. Three Thousand Adolescents Use Smokeless Tobacco.

2. One conclusion reached by the article is that
    A. males are the main users of smokeless tobacco.
    B. use of smokeless tobacco is unrelated to use of other drugs.
    C. users of smokeless tobacco start at a later age than cigarette smokers.
    D. two interviews are necessary for the best study results.
    E. smokeless tobacco use begins in high school.

3. The word *psychoactive* in the passage refers to
    A. all drugs.
    B. pills.
    C. alcohol.
    D. marijuana.
    E. cigarettes.

4. From this study, we may infer that
    A. not many females use drugs.
    B. smoking is an easy habit to break.
    C. smokeless tobacco is less harmful than other forms of tobacco.
    D. users of smokeless tobacco are likely to use other substances.
    E. males use smokeless tobacco to quit smoking cigarettes.

1. **abortive** (ə bôr´ tĭv) *adj.* cut short; fruitless
   The airplane was forced to make an *abortive* landing in the blizzard.
   syn: vain, unsuccessful   *ant:* consummated, successful

2. **accost** (ə kôst´) *verb* to confront; to challenge
   The mugger *accosted* his victims only at night.

3. **acute** (ə kyōōt´) *adj.* serious; sharp
   Boris contracted an *acute* case of food poisoning, which landed him in the hospital.
   syn: critical, crucial   *ant:* dull

4. **debris** (də brē´) *noun* wreckage; ruins
   The *debris* from the hurricane's destruction was spread for miles.
   syn: garbage, junk, rubble

5. **decade** (dĕk´ ād) *noun* a period of ten years
   After a *decade* of obscurity, Richard Nixon again emerged as a political force.

6. **deploy** (dĭ ploi´) *verb* to spread out; to arrange
   During the riot, extra police were *deployed* around the city.

7. **genre** (zhän´ rə) *noun* a kind; sort; style; class
   Of the many different *genres* of literature we studied, I liked poetry the best.
   syn: category

8. **guise** (gīz) *noun* the external appearance
   On Halloween, many children go out in the *guise* of witches.
   syn: aspect, pretext

9. **gusto** (gŭs´ tō) *noun* zest; enthusiasm
   Spot, the tiny dog, ate her treats with great *gusto*.
   syn: enjoyment, zeal   *ant:* disinterest, sluggishness

10. **matron** (mā´ trən) *noun* a woman in charge
    Contrary to my expectations, the *matron* at the prison was a small, slim woman.

11. **meager** (mē´ gər) *adj.* a small amount
    The storm ruined all but a *meager* amount of our food.
    syn: inadequate   *ant:* sufficient

12. **puny** (pyōō′ nē) *adj.* below normal in size and/or strength
Following years of weight-lifting, his *puny* body was transformed greatly.
syn: weak, small   *ant:* massive

13. **quarry** (kwôr′ ē) *noun* the object of a search
Ponce de Leon's *quarry* was the fictitious "fountain of youth."
syn: hunted

14. **sordid** (sôr′ dĭd) *adj.* dirty; filthy
The police uncovered a *sordid* scheme to blackmail the senator.
syn: squalid, dishonorable   *ant:* clean, honorable

15. **spate** (spāt) *noun* a sudden flood or outpouring; series
For a while, a *spate* of killings terrified the community.
syn: flow, rush

Exercise I   Words in Context

Fill in the blanks with the correct vocabulary words needed to complete the sentences.

puny	abortive	debris	matron	genre

A.   There was a great deal of _____ left after the storm. The
_____ rescue effort caused by extreme flooding devastated the
community.

B.   The folk singing _____ long ago gave way to hard rock.

C.   The elderly _____ of the school tightened her rules after the students
were disobedient.

D.   Despite looking _____, Al easily lifted the heavy safe.

sordid	accosted	decade	guise	meager

E.   Sheila tried to leave the _____ neighborhood she lived in, but her
_____ budget made it impossible.

F.   Over the past _____, the outer islands have been _____
by many storms. Some were huge, but others sneaked in, without detection, in the
_____ of a simple thunderstorm.

gusto   **quarry**   **spate**   **acute**   **deploy**

G. The escaped prisoner eluded the police for hours, so they decided to
_____ bloodhounds for assistance. The dogs searched for the man
with _____ and loud barking. Their _____, though,
got away because of a heavy _____ of rain. Even the dogs' well-known,
_____ sense of smell could not help.

Exercise II Roots, Prefixes, and Suffixes

acidic   _____

allergic   _____

meteoric   _____

cosmic   _____

dramatic   _____

1. All the words above end in the suffix –ic, which means "relating to" or "characterized by." Define the words above in the spaces provided.

2. A word like *electronic* has as its literal definition "related to electrons." You may not know that we get electric power from moving *electrons*, but knowing the suffix helps you understand the word. Below, write a list of at least 6 words ending with the suffix –ic.

_____   _____   _____

_____   _____   _____

Exercise III Usage Inferences

Choose the answer that best suits the situation.

1. If your house was destroyed by a fire, what would you do with the *debris*?
    A. make sure it was not still burning
    B. calm it down
    C. bury it
    D. sell it

2. Who might be satisfied with *meager* gifts for a birthday?
    A. a rich child
    B. someone who didn't care about birthdays
    C. a child who had no toys
    D. a person who was very excited

3. Which are most likely not to be considered *sordid*?
    A. a run-down housing project
    B. art galleries
    C. murders
    D. tabloid headlines

Exercise IV Reading Comprehension

Read the selection and answer the questions.

An early NASA study focused on the question, "How can a manned base be established on the moon?" The first step was to perform a Transportation Analysis and determine the most advantageous method of transporting men and materials to the moon and returning the men to earth. All conceivable chemical, nuclear, and ion propulsion systems, using earth and lunar satellites, as well as "direct shot" trajectories, were considered. In addition, every reasonable technical perturbation was considered. *As a result of the analysis, it was conclusively shown that the "direct shot" to the moon, using a five-stage chemically propelled vehicle, is the most desirable.* This was not the expected conclusion, since the establishment and use of a manned earth satellite refueling station has been proposed for many years as the best way for man to travel to the moon. However, these original proposals did not have the benefit of a detailed analysis like the one performed in this study.

The analysis indicated the nuclear propulsion system could not be operational before 1970, so it was not advisable to rely on this system to establish the lunar base. However, if a nuclear system is available as expected, it could be used as indicated on the NASA Master Program Schedule to logistically support the base.

1. The best title for this selection is
   A. Establishment of Moon Proposals.
   B. Analysis of the Moon Proposals.
   C. To the Moon and Back.
   D. Moon Shot Study Points Out Possibilities.
   E. Nuclear Power to Supply Moon Base.

2. A "direct shot" at the moon was
   A. dropped in favor of a five-stage vehicle.
   B. an unexpected conclusion.
   C. attempted previously.
   D. abandoned because of its cost.
   E. possible through nuclear power.

3. The word *perturbation* probably means
   A. variability.
   B. worry.
   C. advancement.
   D. miracle.
   E. mission.

4. NASA implies that nuclear power could provide the energy if that kind of power
   A. were safe.
   B. were ready in time.
   C. would supply the needs of the space craft.
   D. worked best.
   E. The answer cannot be determined.

1. **adverse** (ad vûrs´) *adj.* antagonistic; harmful; unfavorable
   The patient's *adverse* reaction to the medicine nearly killed him.
   syn: impeding, negative   *ant:* positive, satisfactory

2. **culprit** (kŭl´ prĭt) *noun* a guilty or accused person; the source of a problem
   Ellen finally discovered the *culprit* who stole her lunch.
   syn: suspect, offender

3. **detriment** (dĕt´ rə mənt) *noun* a disadvantage; harm
   Color blindness is usually a *detriment* to becoming a pilot.
   syn: drawback, handicap   *ant:* advantage, benefit

4. **facilitate** (fə sĭl´ ĭ tāt) *verb* to ease
   To *facilitate* painting our house, we moved all the furniture into one room.
   syn: help, assist   *ant:* obstruct

5. **gaudy** (gô´ dē) *adj.* tacky; excessively showy
   They filled the gym with many *gaudy* decorations for the spring dance.
   syn: brazen, flashy   *ant:* restrained, tasteful

6. **gazebo** (gə zē´ bō) *noun* a small outdoor building
   Everyone admired the small, beautiful *gazebo* in our backyard.
   syn: summerhouse, pagoda

7. **harass** (hăr´ as) *verb* to bother; to plague
   When the birds swoop down and *harass* the tiny dog, she runs up on the porch.
   syn: badger, hound

8. **irk** (ûrk) *verb* to irritate
   We checked into the hotel, but the dirt left in our room *irked* us greatly.
   syn: annoy

9. **mar** (mär) *verb* to damage; to harm
   One suspension can *mar* your record and hurt your college acceptance chances.
   syn: spoil, scar   *ant:* beautify

10. **mastiff** (măs´ tĭf) *noun* a large breed of dog
    Surprisingly, the prices for the giant *mastiff* and the miniature poodle were the same.

11. **prudent** (prōōd´ nt) *adj.* wise; careful
    The most *prudent* route across the mountains proved to be easier than the others.
    syn: sensible   *ant:* careless

12. **siren** (sī´ rən) *noun* an attractive woman
The latest young movie *siren* to become a star could also act very well.

13. **solace** (sŏl´ əs) *noun* comfort; cheer
A crying infant receives love and *solace* from its mother.
syn: consolation

14. **somber** (sŏm´ bər) *adj.* dark; gloomy
The *somber* weather report predicted a major storm approaching.
syn: bleak   *ant:* cheerful

15. **yen** (yĕn) *noun* a desire
My cat has a strange *yen* for eating corn on the cob.
syn: longing

Exercise I | Words in Context

Fill in the blanks with the correct vocabulary words needed to complete the sentences.

yen	**somber**	**prudent**	**culprit**	**gazebo**

A. The sky grew _____ with the appearance of dark clouds and snow. Winter often gave the whole family a _____ to fly to a tropical island, where they could escape the horrid weather, sit inside a white _____, and soak up the sunshine.

B. "It's never _____ to cheat on an exam," the teacher stated as she stared directly at the suspected _____.

solace	**siren**	**mastiff**	**marred**	**gaudy**

C. The huge _____ strode around the arena like she owned it; her collar, covered with _____ sequins, however, betrayed her as a mere house pet, rather than a champion show dog.

D. The preacher spoke quietly to the crying woman, offering _____ with words from the Bible.

E. My car's windows were totally _____ with soap last Halloween.

F. In ancient times, people believed a tempting _____ could bewitch men.

adverse	detriment	harass	facilitate	irked

G.   All the _____ publicity over the mayor's fine for littering gave the
townspeople the opportunity to _____ him as spokesman for the
"Beautify Our Town" committee. It acted as a(n) _____ to all he
had previously accomplished, which _____ him greatly. His plan to
_____ his political aspirations through environmental issues
backfired on him.

Exercise II Roots, Prefixes, and Suffixes

1.   What root do the following words have in common? What do you think the root means?

motorcycle
cyclable
cyclone
encyclopedia

All the words use the root *cycl*, which means "circle" or "wheel." In the first three, it is
easy to determine the meaning, but it takes a bit of extra thought to understand its use
in *encyclopedia*. How do you suppose the root relates to *encyclopedia*? If you cannot figure out the answer, use a dictionary. _____

2.   The *Cyclades* are a group of islands around another island; *cycles* recur over a regular
period. Name the monster from Greek mythology that has one round eye and takes his
name from this root. _____

3.   Look at the suffixes on the following words and determine what they mean:

outrageous
religious
ridiculous
beauteous
marvelous

The suffixes *–ous*, *–ious*, and *–eous* mean "full of" or "characterized by." Many adjectives
and nouns can be changed by the addition of the suffix. Examples: characterized by vic-
tory (*victorious*); like a felon (*felonious*); full of grief (*grievous*). In the spaces below, list
some words which use the *–ous* endings properly.

_____   _____   _____

_____   _____   _____

Exercise III Usage Inferences

Choose the answer that best suits the situation.

1. In order to *facilitate* getting to the airport, you might
    A. consult the airlines.
    B. read a map.
    C. pack at the last minute.
    D. call for departure times.

2. Which is most *somber*?
    A. singing
    B. funerals
    C. anniversaries
    D. movies

3. Which is an example of *prudent* behavior?
    A. buying lottery tickets
    B. writing test answers in ink
    C. fishing for marlin
    D. wearing seat belts

Exercise IV Reading Comprehension

Read the selection and answer the questions.

Are the penny's days numbered? Will we soon be saying, "a nickel saved is a nickel earned"? The question comes up because Congress is thinking about stopping production of the penny. Some Congressmen say the penny costs the government more money to make than the coin is worth.

A fact-finding federal panel says that getting rid of the one-cent piece would save taxpayers $70 million a year. Every year, more than five billion pennies—that's $50 million—disappear from circulation. Most people find that pennies are too much of a nuisance and end up putting them in piggy banks, dresser drawers, mayonnaise jars, and ashtrays. In effect, people just refuse to use them.

The panel says that the penny is no longer necessary in American business. If the penny were gotten rid of, prices in stores could be rounded off to the nearest nickel, sales taxes could be figured into retail prices, and the penny would no longer be needed.

"Just to replace the ones that go out of circulation is a big job. We have to produce 14 billion pennies a year. That is 78% of all U.S. coins minted annually," said one researcher. Professor Noah Adams, who headed an earlier study, also advised eliminating the penny. "If you look at the total cost of the coin compared to its value, it doesn't pay to make the penny," said Adams.

If the U.S. did abolish the penny, it wouldn't be the first time such a thing has happened. In 1857, production of the American half-cent was stopped because of its low value. In Norway, Brazil, and Argentina, the penny has long been discontinued.

After the 1976 study, Congress decided to change the penny's composition. Previously, pennies had been made mostly of copper. Since 1982, however, pennies have been made of 97% zinc with just a thin coating of copper. The change saved $25 million a year.

Experts continue to point out the advantages of getting rid of the penny altogether. So, why hasn't it been done yet? One argument claims that eliminating the penny would cause inflation. It would cause merchants to round prices up, not down, to the nearest nickel.

Despite all the arguments for getting rid of the penny, it seems likely that it will be around a while longer. Whenever someone proposes eliminating the penny, the nation protests. Apparently, Americans just like certain coins, and don't want change. As Webster says, "There are situations in which pennies are indispensable. When you need one, nothing else will do."

1. Why does the panel recommend getting rid of the penny?
    A. It would save money.
    B. Pennies are not that important for American business.
    C. Prices could be rounded off to a nickel.
    D. Both A and C are correct.
    E. A, B, and C are correct.

2. Who would make the decision to keep or eliminate pennies?
    A. the panel
    B. Noah Adams
    C. the U.S. Mint
    D. Congress
    E. people in general

3. Previously, pennies
    A. had been eliminated in 1857.
    B. cost $70 million a year.
    C. were a "nuisance to carry."
    D. caused inflation.
    E. had been made primarily of copper.

4. Pennies make up what percent of all coins?
    A. 25
    B. 14
    C. 78
    D. 50
    E. 97

1. **amorous**   (am′ ər əs)   *adj.*   of or associated with love
    Rachel was surprised to receive an *amorous* letter from someone she had considered just a friend.
    syn: loving, lustful

2. **devout**   (dĭ vout′)   *adj.*   pious; zealous
    Rita was a *devout* worshipper of God.
    syn: ardent, adoring   *ant:* unholy, irreverent

3. **dexterity**   (dĕk stĕr′ ĭ tē)   *noun*   skill
    The sailor showed his *dexterity* in knot tying.
    syn: expertise   *ant:* clumsiness

4. **frail**   (frāl)   *adj.*   weak; feeble
    Even though Mr. Simians was over eighty, he didn't seem *frail* at all.
    syn: decrepit, fragile   *ant:* solid, strong

5. **garbled**   (gär′ bəld)   *adj.*   distorted; mixed up
    Because the radio picked up two stations at once, the sound was very *garbled*.
    syn: confused; jumbled   *ant:* clear

6. **haven**   (hā′ vən)   *noun*   a place of shelter; sanctuary
    Our house became a *haven* for stray dogs.
    syn: refuge

7. **havoc**   (hav′ ək)   *noun*   ruin; confusion
    The rush-hour accident caused *havoc* for returning motorists.
    syn: calamity, catastrophe

8. **interloper**   (ĭn′ tər lō pər)   *noun*   an intruder
    "Stop changing my work. You're like an *interloper*," yelled the author to his editor.
    syn: meddler

9. **mammoth**   (măm′ əth)   *adj.*   huge
    The earthquake caused *mammoth* destruction throughout China.
    syn: enormous, large   *ant:* tiny

10. **provincial**   (prə vĭn′ shəl)   *adj.*   rural; relating to a province
    The small *provincial* town had a great deal of charm for city people.
    syn: parochial   *ant:* universal

11. **proximity** (prŏk sĭm´ ĭ tē)   *noun*   closeness
    The woodpecker used our feeder, but still stayed in close *proximity* to the trees.
     syn: nearness   *ant:* distance

12. **sanctuary** (sāngk´ chōō ĕr ē)   *noun*   a place of safety; haven
    While it rained, Victor found some *sanctuary* under the trees.
    syn: refuge

13. **sinister** (sĭn´ ĭ stər)   *adj.*   threatening; ominous
    The *sinister* stalker had finally been caught.
    syn: menacing   *ant:* harmless, innocent

14. **skirmish** (skûr´ mĭsh)   *noun*   a small fight; a clash
    We heard the sounds of the *skirmish* as our children played army.
    syn: fray, encounter

15. **wrest** (rĕst)   *verb*   to twist away from
    No one could *wrest* control of the company from its founder.
    syn: wring, extract

Exercise I Words in Context

Fill in the blanks with the correct vocabulary words needed to complete the sentences.

amorous	mammoth	devoutly	garbled	haven

A. I looked out the window and saw two _____ doves, which had obviously
    made a nest in one small area of our _____ barn. The tiny space they oc-
    cupied was a(n) _____ for them against all enemies. Once, I heard their
    _____ peeps as a cat tried to climb in. As much as I like cats, though, I
    was _____ praying for the baby birds' safety.

dexterity	havoc	interloper	frail	sinister

B. The magician's strength and _____ astonished the audience. Then, one
    _____ spectator stood up and exclaimed that she could escape from
    the locked box just as easily. The magician at once led this _____ to the
    stage and gave a(n) _____ wink to the crowd.

C. The hurricane brought _____ and destruction to the island.

wrest	provincial	skirmish	proximity	sanctuary

D.   One _____ after another did little to chase the British troops from their _____ in the heavy, thick woods. The soldiers fought in close _____ to the river, which gave them the advantage over the Colonists.

E.   Long battles were fought in a vain attempt to _____ Philadelphia, the _____ capital of the colonies, from the Americans' hands.

Exercise II Roots, Prefixes, and Suffixes

1.   The Latin root *mort* means "related to death" or "dead," and the word *post* means "after." When a coroner or medical examiner performs a *post-mortem* operation, the doctor is examining a person _____.

2.   List as many words as you can that have *mort* in them.

   _____   _____   _____
   _____   _____   _____

3.   Many words use the root *post*, but in them, it does *not* mean "after." Make a list of some words that use *post* in this way and another in which *post* is used to mean "after." We have done one from each category for you as samples.

   Post meaning "after"   *Post* not meaning "after"
   Postpone   *Postage*

   _____   _____
   _____   _____
   _____   _____

Choose the answer that best suits the situation.

1. In which situation would you need a *haven*?
   A. You need something to remove glue.
   B. It's raining, and you have no umbrella.
   C. Your television is broken.
   D. You do not have to answer a question.

2. Which of the following is most *frail*?
   A. a deer during hunting season
   B. an infant in an incubator
   C. a bicycle with a flat tire
   D. a pregnant woman

3. What would have *sinister* as its most important element?
   A. a lie about curfew
   B. a plot to blow up something
   C. a secret route to safety
   D. a plan to buy a computer

Exercise IV Reading Comprehension

Read the selection and answer the questions.

The United States finds itself in the unusual and highly controversial position of being on the same side of one issue with countries whose policies it usually opposes: the imposition of the death penalty for crimes committed by a juvenile who is tried as an adult. Only Yemen, Iran, Nigeria, Pakistan, and Saudi Arabia—and the "modern" superpower, America—allow such executions; however, the U.S. is the sole country that has actually done so within the recent past. To further differentiate America from other nations, China, which our government strenuously criticizes for its abuses of human rights, has abolished capital punishment for those convictions. The U.S. has signed the International Convention on Civil and Political Rights, which expressly forbids execution of juveniles, but the White House has formally lodged an exception to allow such a policy to exist.

A 26-year-old man awaits lethal injection in Virginia for a murder he committed at age 17. His accomplice in the killing, a 14-year-old girlfriend, was tried as a juvenile and is now free, just as the male participant in the murder waits for death. Many doubts exist as to his sole responsibility and punishment; however, few experts expect clemency to be granted and his sentence commuted to life imprisonment. The primary reason for that belief is Virginia's record of having executed 67 people since 1977, the highest total of any state except Texas.

1.   The primary purpose behind this article was probably to
     A. inform the reader.
     B. persuade the reader.
     C. anger the reader.
     D. save the convict's life.
     E. show the author's outrage.

2.   The only phrase below that does not express an opinion is
     A. imposition of the death penalty.
     B. unusual and highly controversial.
     C. "modern" superpower.
     D. strenuously criticizes.
     E. abuses of human rights.

3.   The author states that the female accomplice was not sentenced to death because of
     A. her age.
     B. doubts over her participation.
     C. her gender.
     D. her relationship to the man.
     E. Both A and B are correct.

4.   The murder
     A. took place last year.
     B. was of two people.
     C. happened in Virginia.
     D. was committed by firearms.
     E. resulted in only one conviction.

1. **authoritarian** (ə thôr ĭ târ´ ē ən) *adj.* dictatorial; strict
It is easier to work for an understanding boss, rather than one who is *authoritarian*.
syn: totalitarian   *ant:* democratic

2. **concise** (kən sīs´) *adj.* short; brief
Many times a *concise* answer is preferable to a long, involved one.
syn: succinct   *ant:* verbose, wordy

3. **conspicuous** (kən spĭk´ yōō əs) *adj.* obvious; clear
We looked out of place and *conspicuous* in tuxedos.
syn: noticeable, showy   *ant:* hidden, ordinary

4. **disparage** (dĭ spar´ ĭj) *verb* to belittle; to abuse
The unethical stock broker *disparaged* the stock even as he was buying it himself.
syn: denigrate   *ant:* compliment

5. **ethics** (ĕth´ ĭks) *noun* morals; principles
Ethics is a way to teach a person right and wrong.
syn: standards, ideals

6. **irrelevant** (ĭ rĕl´ ə vənt) *adj.* not important; beside the point being discussed
I thought that Shakespeare was *irrelevant* to my chosen area of study.
syn: immaterial, inapplicable   *ant:* relevant, germane

7. **jubilant** (jōō´ bə lənt) *adj.* joyous; happy
The *jubilant* lottery winner soon spent her money unwisely.
syn: overjoyed   *ant:* depressed, unhappy

8. **malnutrition** (mal nōō trĭ sh´ ən) *noun* the lack of healthy nutrition
It seems to make no sense, but *malnutrition* frequently makes the stomach swell.

9. **nullify** (nŭl´ ə fī) *verb* to abolish; to negate
Do not *nullify* your fine words with thoughtless behavior.
syn: neutralize

10. **obscure** (ŏb skyōōr´) *adj.* unclear; hidden
Tim knew so many tiny, *obscure* facts that he became a trivia game champion.
syn: indistinct, camouflaged   *ant:* illuminated, clear

11. **permeate** (pûr´ mē āt) *verb* to penetrate; to spread or flow throughout
Environmentalists warned that foreign plants had *permeated* our state.
syn: pervade

12. **retort** (rĭ tôrt´) *noun* a reply; rejoinder
The stand-up comedian had a hilarious *retort* for every heckler.
syn: answer, wisecrack

13. **reverberate** (rĭ vûr´ bə rāt) *verb* to echo
Tarzan's loud call *reverberated* through the jungle.
syn: resound

14. **superficial** (sōō pər fĭsh´ əl) *adj.* shallow; sketchy
The mother assured her crying daughter that the cut was only *superficial*.
syn: cursory, uncritical   *ant:* exhaustive, deep

15. **tertiary** (tur´ shē ĕr ē) *adj.* of third importance
The color of the house was of *tertiary* consideration to the buyers, behind location and size.
syn: unimportant   *ant:* primary

Exercise I Words in Context

Fill in the blanks with the correct vocabulary words needed to complete the sentences.

| obscure | superficial | tertiary | conspicuously | nullify |

A. The treaty was simple to _____ because neither party had put much
thought into the _____ issues. One idea, which had been thought to be
extremely significant, proved to be of _____ importance, behind two
others. Another paragraph was so _____ that no one understood
it completely. The main concept supposedly in the agreement, however, was
_____ absent.

| retorted | reverberated | permeated | jubilant | concise |

B. The newest hit rock song _____ through homes everywhere. The song was
so infectious and _____ that it seemed as though every teenager, and most
parents, listened to it. The song _____ the airwaves from almost all radio
stations in the area. One group, however, dissented and issued a _____
statement claiming that the song was filled with hidden meanings. The band
_____ that the accusation was "nonsense."

| disparaged | ethics | irrelevant | malnutrition | authoritarian |

C. Even though business _____ was taught at the college, most students
thought the course was _____ to their lives. In addition, they
_____ the professor as too strict and _____ for such a course.

D. Many people died of _____ during the famine.

Exercise II Roots, Prefixes, and Suffixes

1. In this lesson, we have included two closely related prefixes. Look at the list and see if you can determine the meaning of the prefixes.

    intercept
    intrastate
    interstellar
    intravenous
    interaction
    intracoastal
    intercontinental
    interior

    The prefix *inter–* means "between," "among," "in the middle of," or "during." The prefix *intra–*, however, means only "within." Answer the following questions:

    A. Does your school have <u>inter</u>mural or <u>intra</u>mural sports?
    B. Does a California "<u>intra</u>state" bus go to Nevada?
    C. Do you receive an "<u>inter</u>venous" injection before an operation?
    D. Does a reporter conduct an "<u>intra</u>view"?
    E. Why wouldn't primitive tribes engage in "<u>intra</u>tribal" raids?
    F. If a football player "<u>intra</u>cepts" a pass, where would he find himself?

    A. _____
    B. _____
    C. _____
    D. _____
    E. _____
    F. _____

2. List 5 more words that begin with the prefix *inter–* or *intra–*

    _____
    _____
    _____
    _____
    _____

Exercise III Usage Inferences

Choose the answer that best suits the situation.

1. Which would be an *obscure* fact?
    A. The Revolutionary War was between England and the Colonies.
    B. Tomatoes were once believed to be poisonous.
    C. Cigarettes can cause cancer.
    D. The earth is round.

2. What would you be *jubilant* about?
    A. a new car
    B. a pet is lost
    C. a dictionary
    D. a clean shirt

3. Which is most likely to *reverberate*?
    A. a dog barking at midnight
    B. a baseball
    C. an argument
    D. an antique boat

Exercise IV Reading Comprehension

Read the selection and answer the questions.

In his book, Mr. Harris explains that the choice of what foods are acceptable to eat within any society is determined by questions of supply and demand. He explains that the foods considered good to eat in any culture are foods that have a more favorable balance of practical benefits over costs. Those foods considered bad to eat, though, have a high direct or indirect cost attached to them.

Harris offered the following example to explain his point. The reason Hindus in India do not eat cows is not that their religion forbids it. Rather, Hinduism has adopted the most sensible eating habits, given the economics of India. Cattle in India are cheap, and the poor people use them for plowing, and they drink their milk. They also burn their manure for heat. If Indians began to eat beef, the price of cattle would rise. These poor people would no longer be able to use them. In a short time, the society would collapse.

Another example is the practice of eating the flesh of horses. Horses have never been raised for meat nor milk in the United States, mainly because other animals such as cattle, pigs, and sheep, are plentiful and less costly to raise. Also, the horse's usefulness as a beast of labor, as well as the practice of horse racing, have led Americans to look on the horse as a sort of pet. To most Americans, the idea of eating a horse is disgusting. This exists, despite the popularity of the common expression, "hungry enough to eat a horse."

Europeans do not share that feeling. After the French Revolution when the poor people rose up against the rich, the idea of the horse as a noble animal that should be protected was destroyed. The peasants saw the horse as a symbol of the rich they hated. They have been eating horses ever since.

1.   According to the author, what determines a society's food preferences?
     A. religion
     B. taste
     C. use and supply
     D. cultural practices
     E. supply and demand

2.   If the poor of India began to eat beef, the author believes
     A. the price would rise.
     B. Indian society might crumble.
     C. horses would replace cows.
     D. Both A and B are correct.
     E. A, B, and C are correct.

3.   One reason Americans do not eat horses is that
     A. horses are shown in movies.
     B. Americans consider the horse dirty.
     C. Americans view horses as noble.
     D. horses are considered pets.
     E. Europeans eat them.

4.   Horses were originally eaten in Europe
     A. during famines.
     B. because of their abundance.
     C. because the horse represented nobility.
     D. because they were a good source of meat.
     E. because they had so many other uses.

1. **bizarre** (bĭ zär´) *adj.* strange; fantastic
   The roller coaster made some *bizarre*, unexpected twists.
   syn: unusual, weird   *ant:* ordinary, regular

2. **bristle** (brĭs´ əl) *verb* to become angry or defensive
   When his idea was rejected, Michael *bristled* and walked out of the meeting.
   syn: fume, seethe

3. **construe** (kən strōō´) *verb* to explain; to interpret a meaning
   The speaker *construed* our silence as approval, but it was really boredom.
   syn: interpret

4. **dubious** (dōō´ bē əs) *adj.* doubtful; arguable
   His claim to the money seemed *dubious* to the judge.
   syn: improbable, unlikely   *ant:* reliable

5. **elapse** (ĭ laps´) *verb* to pass
   Barely an hour had *elapsed* before the thief was caught.

6. **exonerate** (ĭg zŏn´ ə rāt) *verb* to clear of wrongdoing
   DNA evidence was enough to completely *exonerate* the accused.
   syn: absolve, acquit   *ant:* incriminate

7. **fabricate** (fab´ rĭ kāt) *verb* to make up; to construct
   Each time the little boy *fabricated* another lie to explain the previous lie, his parents became angrier.
   syn: devise, concoct

8. **implore** (ĭm plôr´) *verb* to beg; to appeal to
   I *implored* my ex-friend to return the books I had loaned her.
   syn: plead

9. **inhibition** (ĭn hə bĭsh´ ən) *noun* restraint; hindrance
   The driver showed no *inhibitions* about passing the police car.
   syn: discipline, reserve

10. **oratory** (ôr´ ə tôr ē) *noun* speech; the act of speaking well
    Jane showed her skills at *oratory* during the debate.
    syn: elocution, rhetoric

11. **placate** (plā′ kāt) *verb*   to calm; to pacify
The parents gave the spoiled, demanding child candy to *placate* him.
syn: assuage, tranquilize   *ant*: enrage, anger

12. **precipitation** (prĭ sĭp ĭ tā′ shən) *noun*   rain, snow, or hail
Precipitation in the form of snow blanketed the area.

13. **sedate** (sĭ dāt′) *verb*   to tranquilize; to compose
In order to operate on the horse, the veterinarian *sedated* it.
syn: calm   *ant*: agitate

14. **unabated** (ən ə bāt′ əd) *adj.*   unceasing; with undiminished force
The rain fell *unabated* for several days, causing extreme flooding in the town.
syn: continuously   *ant*: lessened, stopped

15. **venomous** (věn′ ə məs) *adj.*   poisonous
Bill was such a cynic that he had a *venomous* remark handy at all times.
syn: toxic   *ant*: harmless

Exercise I Words in Context

Fill in the blanks with the correct vocabulary words needed to complete the sentences.

exonerate	fabricated	bizarre	placate	unabated

A.   Lawyers worked day and night, _____, to prevent their client's execution on what they claimed were _____ charges. The crime had involved
murder with a(n) _____ type of poison. The attorneys had worked for
an entire year to _____ the man wrongly accused. Public opinion, however, differed, and in order to _____ those demanding the death penalty,
the prisoner was kept out of sight.

sedated	dubious	venomous

B.   I was sure the snake was not _____, but when it bit me, I became highly
_____ of that belief. I was rushed to the hospital, _____,
and operated on immediately. I recovered, but that one incident caused me to fear all
snakes.

bristled	construed	oratory	implored
inhibitions	precipitation	elapsed	

C. Mr. Bennett's venom-filled _____ inflamed the people in the audience. They _____ at each racist remark and began to push forward. The police _____ him to end his speech. Bennett, however, _____ the warning as prohibiting his First Amendment rights and declared that he had never before felt any _____ when stating his opinions.

D. Six hours _____ before the heavy _____ stopped. At that point, we had received three feet of snow.

Exercise II Roots, Prefixes, and Suffixes

The suffixes that appear in the following words have opposite meanings. The suffix –*phobia* means "fear of," and –*phobic* refers to a person with a fear. The suffix –*phile* means a "preference for," and –*philiac* describes a person who has that preference.

Here are some words that contain both suffixes:

hydrophobia
hemophiliac
claustrophobic
bibliophile
arachnophobia
Anglophile

The roots of the words are also useful:

biblio	=	book
hydro	=	water
claustro	=	closed in
arachne	=	spider
hemo	=	blood
Anglo	=	English

Now that you know the roots and suffixes, define the words.

A. hydrophobia _____
B. hemophiliac _____
C. claustrophobia _____
D. bibliophile _____
E. Anglophile _____
F. arachnophobia _____

Exercise III Usage Inferences

Choose the answer that best suits the situation.

1.   In which of the following quotations is *implored* used correctly?
     A. "I implored the phone connections properly."
     B. "We implored the audience for quiet."
     C. "The television had been implored before VCRs were invented."
     D. "Many times, our implored had failed."

2.   Which of the following would *exonerate* Peter of a crime?
     A. He confesses.
     B. He escapes.
     C. Someone else confesses.
     D. The victim won't press charges.

3.   What would make Theresa try to *placate* Anna?
     A. Anna felt superior.
     B. Anna was extremely upset.
     C. Theresa blamed Anna for stealing money.
     D. Theresa had been away for a long time.

Exercise IV Reading Comprehension

Read the selection and answer the questions.

Rabies is a disease carried by animals. It is a deadly disease, and any human or animal bitten by a rabid animal is likely to die if treatment is not provided. As early as 2000 B.C., the Greeks recognized that a mad dog, bitten by another mad dog, becomes mad itself.

While rabies had been common in Europe for a long time, most experts think the disease was brought to America during Colonial times. The first case of a mad or rabid dog was reported in Virginia in 1753. It is believed that the dog had been brought from England. Shortly after this, rabies was found in foxes and skunks.

It was not until 1953, however, that rabid raccoons began to appear in Florida. While the first cases were no cause for alarm, it soon became clear that a problem was developing. Like a stain from a spilled soda, the rabid raccoons spread through Georgia, Virginia, West Virginia, and Maryland. By 1988, rabid raccoons were also found in Pennsylvania, Delaware, and the District of Columbia.

Not only are there more cases of rabid raccoons, there are also more reports of rabid cats and dogs. This, of course, makes the danger to humans greater. Humans are more likely to be bitten by a rabid dog or cat than they are likely to be bitten by a rabid raccoon. In fact, there are almost no cases reported of humans having been bitten by raccoons. This may be because most people have the good sense to stay far away from wild animal that appears tame or sick; but, every once in a while, some misguided person will "rescue" a young wild raccoon. In bringing this kind of animal home, in touching it even, the person risks exposing himself and others to this deadly disease. While it is true that people can be treated if bitten by a rabid animal, the treatments are not always 100% successful, and they are always very painful.

In addition to staying away from wild animals, experts warn that you should get your dog or cat vaccinated with a rabies shot. If bitten by any animal, wash the wound thoroughly and see a doctor.

1. The best title for this article might be
    A. Rapid Response Prevents Rabies.
    B. A Short History of Rabies.
    C. Rabies Spreads in U.S.
    D. Rabies, Raccoons, and Humans.
    E. The Bite that Kills.

2. Rabies was first discovered in raccoons in the U.S. in
    A. 1753.
    B. 1953.
    C. Georgia.
    D. 1988.
    E. the 19th century.

3. Which of the following is *not* written or implied in the article?
    A. Most rabies bites are not from raccoons.
    B. Raccoons can give rabies to different kinds of animals.
    C. Treatment for rabies is painful.
    D. Any animal can carry rabies.
    E. A mad dog will foam at the mouth.

4. According to the article, rabies
    A. usually kills if untreated.
    B. began in ancient Greek times.
    C. is caused only by animal bites.
    D. spread throughout the U.S. before the 20th century.
    E. is also called hydrophobia.

1. **arbitrary** (är´ bĭ trĕr ē) *adj.* indiscriminate; impetuous
    The judge's decision was so *arbitrary* that we appealed it.
    syn: erratic, unreasonable *ant*: definite, legitimate

2. **brash** (brăsh) *adj.* hasty; harsh or aggressive
    His *brash* tone of voice surprised us since he was usually so polite.
    syn: impulsive, rash *ant*: polite

3. **doleful** (dōl´ fəl) *adj.* sad; sorrowful
    Her sad, *doleful* look told us she wouldn't be graduating with her class.
    syn: miserable, wretched *ant*: cheerful

4. **fret** (frĕt) *verb* to worry
    The millionaire constantly *fretted* over his investments.
    syn: brood

5. **hypothetical** (hī pə thĕt´ ĭ kəl) *adj.* assumed
    Hypothetical questions begin with "if" and are extremely tricky.
    syn: supposed *ant*: genuine

6. **insurgent** (ĭn sûr´ jənt) *noun* one who revolts
    Most *insurgents* eventually become violent revolutionaries.
    syn: rebel

7. **listless** (lĭst´ lĭs) *adj.* spiritless; uninterested
    The sick, *listless* puppy cried pitifully.
    syn: lackadaisical, indifferent *ant*: active, eager

8. **malady** (măl´ ə dē) *noun* an illness; ailment
    Many *maladies* are preventable by simple cleanliness.
    syn: sickness

9. **morose** (mə rōs´) *adj.* sad; gloomy
    The cat ran away, and its owner was *morose* until it returned.
    syn: sullen *ant*: happy

10. **preclude** (prĭ klōōd´) *verb* to prevent
    A criminal record will *preclude* your becoming a doctor.
    syn: impede *ant*: allow

11. **prelude** (prā′ lōōd) *noun* a preface
"The Star-Spangled Banner" is played as a *prelude* to many sporting events.
syn: beginning   *ant:* finish, epilogue

12. **remote** (rē mōt′) *adj.* distant
Borneo is such a *remote* island that it gets few visitors.
syn: far-off   *ant:* close

13. **subordinate** (sə bôr′ də nət) *adj.* of less importance
The *subordinate* conjunction was punctuated incorrectly.
syn: inferior, secondary   *ant:* superior

14. **tinged** (tĭnjd) *adj.* tinted
The dress was *tinged* with green.
syn: colored

15. **whet** (wĕt) *verb* to sharpen; to stimulate
The smell of steak cooking just *whetted* my appetite.
syn: awaken, hone   *ant:* dull

Exercise I Words in Context

Fill in the blanks with the correct vocabulary words needed to complete the sentences.

fret	malady	listless	insurgent	whet

A.   After the _____ was easily defeated, the victorious soldiers, rather than becoming more enthusiastic, were tired and _____.

B.   "Don't _____; I will find your mother." said the security guard to the lost child.

C.   The carpenter had to _____ the chisel before using it.

D.   One _____ after another forced Marco into the hospital.

morose	remote	tinge	hypothetical	brash

E.   When she realized there was not even a _____ chance of making up with her friends, Roberta became _____ and withdrawn.

F.   At his news conference, the president answered a reporter's _____ ques-
     tion with more than a _____ of sarcasm.

G.   The _____ young boy was frequently punished.

prelude   **preclude**   **subordinates**   **arbitrary**   **doleful**

H.   In order to _____ a long strike, the manager offered a(n)
     _____ pay raise of $1.00 an hour.

I.   Although the general usually treated his _____ kindly, he lashed out at
     them if they made a mistake.

J.   As a(n) _____ to the main course, we have soup and salad.

K.   A long, _____ moan from the monster frightened the audience.

Exercise II Roots, Prefixes, and Suffixes

Review the previous lesson or use a dictionary to define the following words:

A. bibliography   _____
B. hydrosphere   _____
C. hemotoxin   _____
D. Anglo-French   _____
E. arachnid   _____
F. hydrometer   _____
G   Bible   _____
H. hydrodynamics   _____
I. Anglican   _____
J   hydroelectric   _____
K. hemostat   _____

Exercise III Usage Inferences

Choose the answer that best suits the situation.

1. What would be a good *prelude* for your next class in English?
   A. an explanation of grammar
   B. going over test grades
   C. a talk about the material to be covered
   D. a test on punctuation

2. Gabriel *frets* all the time. This might cause
   A. his girlfriend to want more of his time.
   B. him to develop ulcers in the future.
   C. his parents to restrict his television watching.
   D. his coach to let him start as the quarterback.

3. Which of the following would be most likely to make someone an *insurgent*?
   A. satisfaction with life
   B. dissatisfaction with the weather
   C. too much freedom
   D. a dictatorship in his country

Read the selection and answer the questions.

There's a race of men that don't fit in,
   A race that can't stay still;
So they break the hearts of kith and kin,
   And they roam the world at will.
They range the field and they rove the flood,
   And they climb the mountain's crest;
Theirs is the curse of the gypsy blood,
   And they don't know how to rest.

If they just went straight they might go far;
   They are strong and brave and true;
But they're always tired of the things that are,
   And they want the strange and new.
They say: "Could I find my proper groove,
   What a deep mark I would make!"
So they chop and change, and each fresh move
   Is only a fresh mistake.

And each forgets, as he strips and runs
   With a brilliant, fitful pace,
It's the steady, quiet, plodding ones
   Who win in the lifelong race.
And each forgets that his youth has fled,
   Forgets that his prime is past,
Till he stands one day, with a hope that's dead,
   In the glare of the truth at last.

He has failed, he has failed; he has missed his chance;
   He has just done things by half.
Life's been a jolly good joke on him,
   And now is the time to laugh.
Ha, ha! He is one of the Legion Lost;
   He was never meant to win;
He's a rolling stone, and it's bred in the bone;
   He's a man who won't fit in.

                                        —Robert Service

1. The best title for this poem would be
    A. Gypsy Blood.
    B. A Rolling Stone.
    C. The Men That Don't Fit In.
    D. Stay Put and Prosper.
    E. Lost Legions Lose.

2. In stanza 1, the word *race* means
    A. contest.
    B. ethnic group.
    C. particular type.
    D. onward movement.
    E. All of the above are correct.

3. The best re-stating of the point of the poem is
    A. constant change brings happiness.
    B. people desiring new places to live will never find them.
    C. it is better to wander than it is to stay still.
    D. those who continually seek new experiences will only be unhappy.
    E. life passes you by if you don't try new experiences.

4. According to the poem, people who wander the world
    A. suffer from a curse.
    B. believe in their abilities.
    C. cannot be satisfied.
    D. are overtaken by steady, direct people.
    E. All of the above are correct.

1. **ascend** (ə sĕnd´) *verb* to climb
   The old man took the elevator rather than try to *ascend* by the steps.
   syn: mount   *ant:* descend

2. **convalesce** (kŏn´ və lĕs) *verb* to recover
   Tom had a long period to *convalesce* after his accident.
   syn: improve, recuperate   *ant:* deteriorate

3. **dregs** (drĕgs) *noun* the least valuable part
   Most people have little use for those whom they view as the *dregs* of society.

4. **falter** (fôl´ tər) *verb* to hesitate; to halt
   Terrible weather caused the expedition to *falter* in its quest.
   syn: waver   *ant:* persevere

5. **fitful** (fĭt´ fəl) *adj.* intermittent; sporadic
   Nightmares made for a *fitful* night's sleep.
   syn: interrupted, irregular   *ant:* constant

6. **incoherent** (ĭn kō hîr´ ənt) *adj.* unclear; disjointed
   After being sedated, he mumbled in an *incoherent* way about a variety of subjects.
   syn: muddled, disorganized   *ant:* orderly, clear

7. **intemperate** (ĭn tĕm´ pər ĭt) *adj.* unwise; excessive
   Making *intemperate* comments about Stalin in Russia meant certain imprisonment.
   syn: unrestrained, unbridled   *ant:* constrained

8. **irate** (ī rāt´) *adj.* angry
   He called the Better Business Bureau because he was *irate* about being swindled.
   syn: furious   *ant:* happy

9. **octogenarian** (ŏk tə jə nâr´ ē ən) *noun* someone in his or her eighties
   Many *octogenarians* are still alert and active.

10. **painstaking** (pānz´ tā kĭng) *adj.* careful; conscientious
    Creating a detailed model of the historical warship was a *painstaking* process.
    syn: meticulous   *ant:* careless

11. **reprehensible** (rĕp rĭ hĕn´ sə bəl)   *adj.*   deserving of rebuke
I believe that lying is more *reprehensible* than stealing is.
syn: blameworthy   *ant:* praiseworthy

12. **respite** (rĕs´ pĭt)   *noun*   a rest; a short break
They needed a *respite* from work, so they went on a vacation.
syn: time-out, reprieve

13. **restrictive** (rĭ strĭk´ tĭv)   *adj.*   limiting
Our curfew felt more *restrictive* than it actually was.
syn: narrowed

14. **stagnate** (stag´ nāt)   *verb*   to stop developing
If you let your children sit in front of the television all day, they will *stagnate*.
syn: stifle   *ant:* flourish

15. **stereotype** (stĕr´ ē ə tīp)   *noun*   a cliché; an oversimplified concept or image
The *stereotype* of a pitbull is a dog that is always mean and dangerous.
syn: generalization

Exercise I   Words in Context

Fill in the blanks with the correct vocabulary words needed to complete the sentences.

incoherent	**falter**	**irate**	**painstaking**	**reprehensible**

A.   The officer could not understand the _____ man's explanation for his
_____ behavior.

B.   The tightrope walker did not _____ when his long pole fell; completing
the act without it, however, proved to be _____ work.

C.   I was _____ about the ticket price for the show, but I went anyway.

restrictive	**convalescence**	**octogenarian**	**fitful**	**stereotype**

D.   When the _____ night had passed, the wrinkled _____
demanded that the nurse at the hospital remove his _____ bandaging at
once. The old man was not the typical _____ of a weak, frail 85-year-old.

E.   A long _____ is needed after you break a bone.

| respite | stagnated | ascend | dregs | intemperate |

F. "Cease your _____ remarks immediately," said the judge, "or I'll send you to jail for contempt of court."

G. While the tourist was determined to _____ the lighthouse, he looked for any moment _____ from the task.

H. Wine is usually missing the _____ at the bottom if it has been strained.

I. After ten years at his job, David felt that his career had _____, so he found one with more potential for growth.

Exercise II Roots, Prefixes, and Suffixes

1. Place these words with prefixes that refer to numbers in the correct numerical order.

A. binomial   1. _____
B. decade   2. _____
C. octagon   3. _____
D. triangle   4. _____
E. unicycle   5. _____
F. quintet   6. _____
G. nonagenarian   7. _____
H. quadruplets   8. _____
I. sextuplets   9. _____
J. septennial   10. _____

2. Use a dictionary to find one word for each Latin prefix used in the words above.

1. _____   6. _____
2. _____   7. _____
3. _____   8. _____
4. _____   9. _____
5. _____   10. _____

Exercise III Usage Inferences

Choose the answer that best suits the situation.

1. Which is the most *reprehensible* act?
    A. contributing to the cancer society
    B. making obscene phone calls
    C. thievery and burglary
    D. political assassination

2. Which of the following would require *convalescence* afterwards?
    A. a car accident
    B. failing a test
    C. cutting a finger
    D. lack of sleep

3. Which would most likely be *fitful*?
    A. the effect of gravity
    B. the discovery of uranium
    C. a disinterested student's study habits
    D. life inside a beehive during winter

Exercise IV Reading Comprehension

Read the selection and answer the questions.

Paul Burbutis, a professor of entomology at the University of Delaware, has spent 15 years seeking a way to control one of the world's most destructive agricultural pests, the corn borer. Now, he has found a small black wasp that he thinks might do the job.

"The corn borer is a small, flesh-colored caterpillar about an inch long," said Dr. Burbutis. "It causes between 1 million and 2 million dollars worth of damage on Delaware corn farms each year. We can control it with heavy coatings of insecticides, but that gets very expensive. As you know, insecticides are also bad for the environment."

Dr. Burbutis explained that the corn borer got its name because the young insects bore their way into the base of the ears of corn. Once there, they form cocoons. They then emerge from the cocoons about a week later as fully grown moths.

The black wasp that Dr. Burbutis is working with is a natural enemy of corn borers. "The wasps are so small that 25 could fit on the head of a pin," said Dr. Burbutis. "The female lays its eggs inside the corn borer's eggs. Then, the young wasp eats the inside out of the borer's egg and spins a cocoon. In effect, it makes the corn borer's egg its own home." Naturally, this destroys the corn borer.

Dr. Burbutis hopes someday to be able to breed the black wasps by the hundreds of millions in factories. This would result in the making of a living insecticide. The wasps could then be sprayed on fields, just as an insecticide is. Unfortunately, the only way to breed the wasps at present is to breed large amounts of borer eggs. The wasps eat nothing else. "We're trying to come up with a method to artificially duplicate the borer eggs. But more research needs to be done," said Dr. Burbutis.

Scientists don't expect the wasps to entirely wipe out the corn borer population even if they do find a way to breed the wasps in large numbers. For one thing, other insects eat the wasps themselves. One such insect is the common ladybug. But scientists do see the wasp as one part of a total plan.

Another enemy of the corn corer is the disgusting Lydella Thompsoni fly. This insect bears its young outside the holes of corn borers. "The young flies burrow into the bodies of the borers. There they live like maggots, until they are ready to crawl out and become adult flies," said Dr. Burbutis. "By then, the borers are no more." Scientists made an attempt to control borers in the 1940s by releasing millions of the Lydella flies. But for some unknown reason, the flies had disappeared by 1958. Years later, another attempt to establish them was begun, but thus far, the results are not known.

1. The best title for this selection is
    A. Insect Pests.
    B. Control of Corn Borers.
    C. New Attempt at Pest Control.
    D. A Living Insecticide.
    E. Dr. Burbutis's Experiments.

2. The corn borer
    A. is extremely small.
    B. gets its name from where its young live.
    C. causes over $2 million in crop damage.
    D. will be eliminated by wasps.
    E. All of the above are correct.

3. The wasps and flies described in the article
    A. both eat the mature corn borer.
    B. are attempts to control the corn borer.
    C. are easily bred.
    D. get eaten by ladybugs.
    E. Both A and B are correct.

4. Lydella Thompsoni flies
    A. were released previously, but have disappeared.
    B. are ineffective in controlling corn borers.
    C. are an expensive method of pest control.
    D. were discovered by Dr. Burbutis.
    E. kill corn borers the same way as black flies do.

Lesson Sixteen

1. **articulate** (är tĭk´ yə lĭt) *adj.* well-spoken; clear
   He was one of our most *articulate* presidents, one who could clearly explain complicated problems.
   syn: eloquent   *ant:* inarticulate, unintelligible

2. **cant** (kănt) *noun* a specific language or vocabulary
   Juan changed his major from philosophy because he could no longer understand the *cant* of his professor.
   syn: terminology

3. **clemency** (klĕm´ ən sē) *noun* mercy; leniency
   The governor granted the convicted murderer *clemency* just prior to her execution.
   syn: forgiveness   *ant:* harshness

4. **eminent** (ĕm´ ə nənt) *adj.* famous; prominent
   The *eminent* politician delivered the commencement address at graduation.
   syn: renowned, famed   *ant:* unknown, common

5. **exploits** (ĕk´ sploits) *noun* adventures; achievements
   The travel book chronicles the brave *exploits* of people in primitive places.
   syn: feats

6. **immaterial** (ĭm mə tîr´ ē əl) *adj.* irrelevant; not pertaining
   The judge ruled that the girlfriend's testimony was *immaterial*, and the case was quickly lost.
   syn: unrelated, unsubstantial   *ant:* important

7. **interrogate** (ĭn tĕr´ ə gāt) *verb* to question
   When she came home after curfew, Kate's parents *interrogated* her about where she'd been.
   syn: quiz

8. **kindle** (kĭnd´ l) *verb* to light, to stir up
   Even though Robert had not seen Camellia for twenty years, the sight of her *rekindled* all the old feelings.
   syn: ignite   *ant:* extinguish

9. **pittance** (pĭt´ ns) *noun* a small amount
   He had to get a new job because he had only a *pittance* left in his bank account.
   syn: trace, smidgen   *ant:* abundance

10. **pragmatic** (prăg măt´ ĭk) *adj.* practical; down-to-earth
He is a *pragmatic* person who knows how to get the job done.
syn: realistic   *ant:* idealistic

11. **rampart** (ram´ pärt) *noun* a defensive structure
A dozen enemy troops stormed the castle *ramparts*.
syn: stronghold, bulwark

12. **retract** (rĭ trăkt´) *verb* to pull back or in
I saw Fluffy the cat *retract* her claws just after she was done scratching the couch.
syn: withdraw   *ant:* project

13. **talon** (tăl´ ən) *noun* a claw
We could see that the small animal could not escape the eagle's *talons*.

14. **wince** (wĭns) *verb* to flinch
The doctor noticed that his patients seemed to *wince* when he gave them their injections.
syn: cringe

15. **writhe** (rīth) *verb* to twist; to wriggle
The kite's long tail *writhed* about as if it were a real serpent.
syn: squirm

Exercise I Words in Context

Fill in the blanks with the correct vocabulary words needed to complete the sentences.

rampart	retract	pittance	eminent	interrogate

A. Although he was guilty as charged, the _____ politician refused to let the police _____ him yet, for fear he would say something he later would be forced to _____.

B. Only a(n) _____ existed in the Royal Treasury, so the queen decided to tax her subjects more in order to build another _____ on her castle.

exploits	kindle	clemency	pragmatic	writhed

C.   It was nearly impossible for the Cub Scout to re_____ the fire.

D.   I prefer _____ results from your experiments rather than
     _____ their own sake.

E.   The _____ board refused to hear the murderer's appeal.

F.   The quarterback _____ in agony with a broken leg.

articulate	cant	immaterial	wince	talons

G.   The hawk used its powerful _____ to perch on the trainer's arm.

H.   He kept trying to _____ his feelings to the psychiatrist, even though
     they were _____ to the topic being discussed.

I.   Although Alicia was an atheist, she tried not to _____ when her religion
     teacher talked about the Bible. Alicia believed none of that _____
     anymore.

Exercise II Roots, Prefixes, and Suffixes

The roots *vit* and *viv* both "mean to live." They are used in words such as:

survive
revived
vital
vivisection
revitalized
vivid

Fill in the blanks with the words listed above to complete the sentences.

A.   I have a _____ memory of the horrible _____ of a frog
     performed in biology class.

B.   In order to _____, I gathered all the _____ equipment.

C.   The water had _____ our strength; we crossed the desert with
     _____ energy.

Exercise III Usage Inferences

Choose the answer that best suits the situation.

1. A musician might *wince* from
    A. having to practice for a concert.
    B. hearing a series of off-key notes.
    C. misplacing a favorite violin.
    D. the conductor's praise.

2. The best example of *pragmatic* behavior is
    A. remembering where your keys are.
    B. planting a tomato.
    C. not studying for a test.
    D. saving money for retirement.

3. Which quotation below would be related to something *immaterial*?
    A. "I'm sorry, but there's no excuse for that."
    B. "James broke it, not I."
    C. "Stick to the point."
    D. "I know the answer."

Exercise IV Reading Comprehension

Read the selection and answer the questions.

Turpan, China, is one of the hottest and driest towns in the world. In mid-summer, the air temperature ranges from 104 to 120 degrees. But the temperature of the ground can rise even higher than that. At times, it goes above 170 degrees. Less that half an inch of rain falls on the area in a year. Most of the rain that falls evaporates before it hits the ground. Yet, despite these terrible conditions, Turpan grows some of the finest melons, grapes, and cotton in the world. In so doing, it supports a population of 186,000 people.

Turpan's secret is a 2,000-year-old system of underground wells and tunnels. These tunnels extend over a combined distance of 1,000 miles under the desert floor. This irrigation system is called the "karez." The entire system collects water that flows down from melting icecaps on top of the Tien Shan mountains.

As ice melts on top of the mountains, water flows downward through a series of wells towards the valley. If it flowed along the blazing hot desert surface, it would evaporate. But the temperature in the underground canals is low enough to prevent this from happening. Mohammed Liu explains that work on the karez was begun about 2,000 years ago. "The first wells were dug out by hand," he explained. "Most of those built centuries ago are still in use."

The karez is not the only way in which the people of the area have fought the desert climate. Every house in Turpan has a basement beneath it. It is here people go to escape the midday heat. After the sun goes down, they come out to sleep on the flat rooftops. Here, they can catch whatever breezes might be stirring.

As successful as it is, work on the karez continues. "We are reinforcing the tunnels with concrete pipe," said Liu. "Now they should last another 2,000 years. We are also surrounding the fields and vineyards with 10,000 acres of trees and brush. The trees and bushes will protect the crops from sandstorms."

Turpan today stands as an example of man's determination to find a way to survive in the most unlikely places; places such as Turpan, where man must deal with heat, sandstorms, and dryness, stand as monuments to man's strength, brains, and determination.

1. The best title for the article is
    A. Life in Turpan.
    B. Melons Sustain Life in Desert.
    C. Survival Amid Adversity.
    D. How to Live in the Desert.
    E. Liu Explains Turpan.

2. What happens to most of the rain that actually does fall in and around Turpan?
    A. It is collected in wells.
    B. It evaporates.
    C. It falls on the mountains.
    D. The article does not explain.
    E. Both A and C are correct.

3. The karez
    A. extends for more than 2,000 miles.
    B. is a series of mountains.
    C. was dug to irrigate Turpan's crops.
    D. needs protection from the sandstorms.
    E. is a system of cooling units.

4. It can be assumed that Liu
    A. is an architect.
    B. is a town official.
    C. helped build the karez.
    D. works underground.
    E. None of the above is correct.

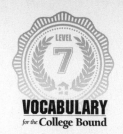

Lesson Seventeen

1. **aspirant** (ăs′ pər ənt)   *noun*   a candidate
   Only one *aspirant* for the class drama production showed up.
   syn: applicant

2. **engrossed** (ĕn grōsd′)   *adj.*   deeply involved; occupied
   Once he became *engrossed* in a book, few things interrupted him.
   syn: absorbed   *ant:* distracted

3. **flamboyant** (flăm boi′ ənt)   *adj.*   showy; ostentatious
   Ford introduced a line of *flamboyant* colors in its new models.
   syn: flashy, garish   *ant:* plain, simple

4. **improvise** (ĭm′ prə vīz)   *verb*   to make up on the spot
   If he didn't know the answer, Michael often *improvised* one.
   syn: extemporize

5. **impunity** (ĭm pyōō′ nĭ tē)   *noun*   exemption from punishment
   The thief kept stealing with *impunity* as if he would never be caught.
   syn: immunity   *ant:* culpability

6. **indigent** (ĭn′ dĭ jĭnt)   *adj.*   poor, destitute
   Many *indigent* men lined up, hoping to be hired for the few available jobs.
   syn: penniless   ant: affluent

7. **opportune** (ŏp ər tōōn′)   *adj.*   favorable; suitable
   The pause in the conversation gave Randall an *opportune* moment to state his opinion.
   syn: fortunate

8. **prodigy** (prŏd′ ə jē)   *noun*   a phenomenon
   The musical competition was won by an older violinist, not by the child *prodigy*.
   syn: marvel

9. **profound** (prə found′)   *adj.*   major; deep
   Although the twins were identical, they exhibited *profound* personality differences.
   syn: intense

10. **rail** (rāl)   *verb*   to complain bitterly
    The farmer *railed* and yelled to the heavens about the flood that destroyed his crop.
    syn: shriek

11. **regatta** (rĭ gä′ tə) *noun* a boat race
Almost anyone with a boat entered the *regatta* held last summer.

12. **shun** (shᵃn) *verb* to reject; to snub
According to some religious beliefs, members must *shun* outsiders.
syn: scorn, avoid   *ant:* accept, welcome

13. **subterranean** (sub tə rā′ nē ən) *adj.* underground
White alligators are rumored to live in the *subterranean* sewer system of New York.

14. **succumb** (sə kŭm′) *verb* to yield; to submit
After weeks of constant bombing, the enemy finally *succumbed* to our overwhelming force.
syn: relent, give in   *ant:* overcome

15. **viable** (vī′ ə bəl) *adj.* capable of living; achievable
No one thought the tree that was struck by lightning would survive, but it was quite *viable*.
syn: living, feasible   *ant:* dead, impossible

Fill in the blanks with the correct vocabulary words needed to complete the sentences.

| engrossed | improvise | shun | subterranean | profound |

A.   The group of moles was wary. Because of the traps, they had to _____ all their usual _____ mazes of tunnels.

B.   Since Albert hadn't studied, he tried to _____ an answer. _____ in his own reply, he didn't notice the rest of the class smirking at what he thought were _____ comments.

| regatta | rail | prodigy | viable | impunity |

C.   Until they are caught, most criminals think they can commit their crimes with complete _____.

D.   The only _____ entry left in the _____ was a sleek, two-mast sailboat.

E.   The foreman of the plant would frequently _____ for hours about his workers' sloppiness.

F.   When James performed on the piano at age eight, the critics called him a(n) _____.

| aspirant | flamboyant | opportune | indigent | succumbed |

G.   No one came to visit the sickly, _____ man in the hospital. When he finally _____ to cancer, he died alone.

H.   The general decided that the most _____ time to launch an invasion was at dawn.

I.   The wrestler looked _____ in his red and gold robes.

J.   Every _____ to win an Olympic Medal must train rigorously for years.

The following is a list of prefixes, roots, and suffixes that have been presented in Lessons 1-16. As a review, find or create words that use combinations of these prefixes, roots, and suffixes. Write a definition for each word, including the ones you have made up yourself. We have done three for you.

Prefixes	Roots	Suffixes
in–	*tech*	*–able*
un–	*vert*	*–ible*
dis–	*contra*	*–ism*
trans–	*terr*	*–ary*
hypo–	*cycl*	*–ic*
hyper–	*hydro*	*–ous*
pre–	*hemo*	*–phobia*
intra–	*claustro*	*–phile*
inter–	*bibl*	
uni–	*arach*	
bi–	*anglo*	
tri–	*viv*	
quad–		
quint–		
sex–		
sep–		
oct–		
nona–		
dec–		

biterrism   -   related to two lands
cyclous   -   like a circle
incontrovertible   -   not able to be turned against

1. _____ - _____
2. _____ - _____
3. _____ - _____
4. _____ - _____
5. _____ - _____
6. _____ - _____
7. _____ - _____
8. _____ - _____
9. _____ - _____
10. _____ - _____

Exercise III Usage Inferences

Choose the answer that best suits the situation.

1. Which person would be exhibiting *improvisation*?
    A. John put together the lawnmower by himself.
    B. Tom didn't read from the prepared script.
    C. Alicia went out for a sundae.
    D. Lisa could finally work the computer.

2. Which would be most *flamboyant* out of the following?
    A. spending money for a face-lift
    B. wearing a tux to the prom
    C. dyeing your hair orange
    D. writing test answers in red ink

3. What might a person *succumb* to?
    A. royalty
    B. illness
    C. travel
    D. happiness

Exercise IV Reading Comprehension

Read the selection and answer the questions.

One nuclear agency, headed by William Martin of the U.S., is currently working on a new project called Agent Defeat Weapons Concept Exploration. The end result is to destroy stockpiles of an enemy's biological or chemical weapons, while not also killing people, leaving soldiers without the means to continue to wage war. This would be the first truly "new" weapon since the Atomic Bomb.

Interviews have revealed that the development has been daunting and has been underway in complete secrecy. Previously, our apparent enemy would have been the Soviet Union; now, however, an all-out nuclear war is less likely, and America's 65,000 nuclear weapons would be essentially useless against small groups of terrorists. Consequently, a new approach is necessary.

Many methods have been explored by the scientists working on the project, including lasers, vibrating bombs, sticky gels, foams, and air-sprayed acids. Each new solution posed new problems. For example, sticky gels could have been bombed on enemies' bunkers, preventing soldiers from entering. That solution was quickly abandoned because of countermeasures to render the gel useless, regardless of its initial stickiness. Ozone was considered, also, but because it cannot be stored for a long while, it, too, was eliminated from consideration as a solution.

Finally, six concepts were given approval for final testing, as long as they could meet three criteria: cost, effectiveness, and ability to counter a wide array of chemical and biological weapons. After testing, only the vibrating bomb, which produces extremely low-level sounds, below human ability to hear, seems to work well enough to merit further consideration. The sounds produced break down chemicals, such as gases, and diseases, such as anthrax, into harmless particles.

The major problem plaguing the entire project, though, seems to be that it is entirely dependent on a potential enemy not improving its weapons protection capabilities, and that is one aspect scientists cannot predict accurately.

1. The best title for this article would be
   A. New Weapons Under Development.
   B. Destroying Enemies.
   C. Vibrating Bomb Works Well.
   D. Project to Kill Weapons, Save Lives.
   E. Space-Age Weapons.

2. According to the article,
   A. the vibrating bomb works best.
   B. many problems exist in each solution.
   C. cost is a factor in determining which weapons to develop.
   D. America had prepared to fight a nuclear war in the past.
   E. All of the above are correct.

3. The three elements necessary for approval in the final phase are:
   A. potential, cost, and range.
   B. effectiveness, money, and safety.
   C. what's destroyed, difficulty to make, amount of money necessary.
   D. ability to not kill people, ease of use, and cost.
   E. None of the above is correct.

4. What is one difference between how war was prepared for previously and the new developments?
   A. Previous wars have been nuclear.
   B. Cities were the main targets.
   C. Only soldiers were destroyed.
   D. Attempts are being made to ruin an enemy's desire to fight.
   E. The enemy may be a group, not a nation.

1. **acute** (ə kyūt´) *adj.* being less than ninety degrees
    The teacher asked one student to draw an *acute* angle and another to draw a right angle on the whiteboard.

2. **adjacent** (ə jā´ sənt) *adj.* next to
    Which two numbers are *adjacent* to your new address?
    syn: nearby   *ant:* remote, distant

3. **axiom** (ăk´ sē əm) *noun* a true statement that needs no proof; something accepted as true
    It is accepted as an *axiom* that if the demand for a product increases, the price will also increase.

4. **bisect** (bī´ sĕkt) *verb* to cut into two equal or similar pieces
    In order to *bisect* the circle, Evan drew a straight line directly through the center from the edges.

5. **circumference** (sûr kəm´ frəns) *noun* the distance around the outside of a curved object that has no opening
    As anyone can see, the *circumference* of a basketball is much larger than that of a baseball.
    syn: perimeter

6. **congruent** (kän grōō´ ənt) *adj.* having the same size and shape
    He placed one square directly on top of another, and it looked as if there was only one; therefore, the squares were *congruent*.
    syn: coinciding

7. **diameter** (dī ăm´ ə tər) *noun* a straight line through the center of a circle or sphere
    The moon has a *diameter* of 2,159 miles, but the earth's is 7,918 miles.

8. **empirical** (ĕm pēr´ ə kəl) *adj.* based or relying on experience, observation, or experiment
    Based on the *empirical* evidence she gathered from living in Alaska, if the temperature is more than twenty below zero, traveling outside is extremely dangerous.
    syn: factual   *ant:* theoretical

9. **geometry** (jē ăm´ ə trē) *noun* the mathematical study of shape, size, and position of figures
    After I studied *geometry,* the next math course I had to take before I could graduate was algebra.

10. **horizontal** (här ə zän´ təl)   *adj.*   flat, level, and parallel to the horizon
The storm knocked over the huge tree, and it is now completely *horizontal*.

11. **integer** (ĭn´ tə jər)   *noun*   a number that has no fractions or decimal points
How many *integers* are between eight and eighteen?
syn: number

12. **parallel** (pă´ rə ləl)   *adj.*   lines that are the same distance apart and never meet
You see an optical illusion when you look down a straight road and the *parallel* sides
seem to meet in the distance.

13. **perpendicular** (pər pĕn dĭk´ yĭ lər)   *adj.*   intersecting or forming a right angle
Most tall buildings are made so that they are perfectly *perpendicular* to the ground.

14. **ratio** (rā´ shē ō)   *noun*   a comparison or proportion between different things
There are thirty people at the party—twenty children and ten parents; the *ratio* of
children to parents, therefore, is two to one.
syn: relationship

15. **theorem** (thēr´ əm)   *noun*   a statement that can be proven to be true by logical
reasoning
The Pythagorean *theorem* can be applied only to triangles that have a right angle.
syn: principle

Fill in the blanks with the correct vocabulary words needed to complete the sentences.

| **circumference** | **ratio** | **geometry** | **diameter** | **integers** |

A.   When I had my new house built, my wife wanted a round pool with a _____ of twenty feet so she could swim and get some exercise. She didn't realize that size would mean the pool's _____ would be only slightly larger than six feet. She didn't believe me, so I explained that the _____ between the two _____ of ten and twenty was based on pi. Dividing twenty by pi gave me the number six. She told me that when she went to school, _____ wasn't required.

| **parallel** | **horizontally** | **bisect** | **adjacent** |

B.   The community group finally agreed to allow the road to _____ their small town, nearly dividing it in half, but they demanded three conditions. One condition was that the road had to run in a manner that was _____ to a farmer's land and not cut into it. The second requirement was that no billboards could be set up _____ to the old oak tree. The final demand was that all street signs must hang _____ from wires stretched across the road.

| **axiom** | **perpendicular** | **acute** | **empirical** |

C.   The first _____ of good sportsmanship is to be a good winner.

D.   All the _____ data proves that an earthquake struck and knocked down all the buildings.

E.   No _____ triangle can include any _____ lines; if it does, it must be a right triangle.

| **theorem** | **congruent** |

F.   Those two houses would be completely _____, but one has a small chimney.

G.   A common _____ in painting is that mixing red and blue will create purple.

Exercise II Roots, Prefixes, and Suffixes

1. What root do the following words have in common? What do you think it means?

    pendant
    pendulum
    dependent

    The root is *pend*, which means "hang" or "weigh." For example, a *pendant* is a piece of jewelry that hangs from the neck.

    List at least 3 more words that include the root *pend*.

    1. _____
    2. _____
    3. _____

2. The root *rat* means "computation" or "reason." The prefix *ir–* means "not" or "the opposite of." Using the root *rat* and the prefix *ir–*, list a word that describes someone who is not being reasonable. _____

3. The suffix *–al* means "pertaining or referring to." For example, something that pertains to comedy is *comical*. List 5 other words that use the suffix *–al*.

    1. _____
    2. _____
    3. _____
    4. _____
    5. _____

Exercise III Usage Inferences

Choose the answer that best suits the situation.

1. Which sentence is describing something through a *ratio*?
    A. I can see the two boats far off in the distance.
    B. The boats are approaching us, and I hear the motors.
    C. The boat looks very large, but it's too far away to tell for sure.
    D. I can tell that this boat is twice as large as the other one.

2. Which situation is the best example of *bisect*?
    A. The sharpshooter hit the center of the target twice in a row.
    B. The doctor had to cut through the patient's arm to save him.
    C. The apple pie was split equally between my brother and sister.
    D. The book has 200 pages, but I was able to read only a hundred.

3. Which statement best shows the proper use of the word *empirical*?
   A. The decision to kill the insects was based entirely on empirical observations about them.
   B. It is empirical for you to learn how to learn to drive better because you can easily cause an accident.
   C. One empirical and dedicated person is enough to sway people's opinions about war and peace.
   D. The empirical city controlled all the surrounding countryside through the use of threats.

Exercise IV Reading Comprehension

Read the selection and answer the questions.

THESE are the times that try men's souls. The summer soldier and the sunshine patriot will, in this crisis, shrink from the service of their country; but he that stands by it now, deserves the love and thanks of man and woman. Tyranny, like hell, is not easily conquered; yet we have this consolation with us, that the harder the conflict, the more glorious the triumph. What we obtain too cheap, we esteem too lightly: it is dearness only that gives every thing its value. Heaven knows how to put a proper price upon its goods; and it would be strange indeed if so celestial an article as FREEDOM should not be highly rated. Britain, with an army to enforce her tyranny, has declared that she has a right (not only to TAX) but "to BIND us in ALL CASES WHATSOEVER" and if being bound in that manner, is not slavery, then is there not such a thing as slavery upon earth. Even the expression is impious; for so unlimited a power can belong only to God.

Whether the independence of the continent was declared too soon, or delayed too long, I will not now enter into as an argument; my own simple opinion is, that had it been eight months earlier, it would have been much better. We did not make a proper use of last winter, neither could we, while we were in a dependent state. However, the fault, if it were one, was all our own; we have none to blame but ourselves. But no great deal is lost yet.

–Thomas Paine

1. What is the main point Paine is attempting to convey about the situation that the American Colonies find themselves in?
   A. There is still time to win independence from England.
   B. Someone who supports freedom when there is a crisis is a patriot.
   C. Declaring independence from England was wrong.
   D. Freedom is important, but war is usually deadly.
   E. England has no right to try to rule America.

2. Who are "the summer soldier and the sunshine patriot"?
   A. people in Britain opposed to American independence
   B. people in Britain who want independence for America
   C. colonists not willing to fight for independence
   D. the men who are already serving in the Continental Army
   E. the colonists who will fight but only in good weather

3. What would be the best definition of *impious*, as it is used in the passage?
   A. not religious
   B. using insults
   C. being devout
   D. showing admiration
   E. being disobedient

4. Based on what he says in this essay, which statement would Paine most likely agree with?
   A. Slavery occurs whenever one nation rules another.
   B. All citizens in the colonies want freedom from England.
   C. Britain's laws should be obeyed until independence.
   D. Freedom is necessary because it is God-given.
   E. Things that people win easily have no real value.